Museums and the public understanding of science

Museums
and the public
understanding
of science

Edited by John Durant

Science Museum
in association with the Committee
on the Public Understanding of Science

The Science Museum is grateful to the Committee on the
Public Understanding of Science for financial support
without which publication would not have been possible,
and to Victoria Smith for editing and laying out the papers.

Published 1992.

Set from Pagemaker in Postscript Monotype Plantin Light
to a design style by Ken Garland and Associates.
Printed in England by Antony Rowe Ltd, Chippenham,
Wilts.

ISBN 0 901805 49 1

Science Museum, Exhibition Road, London SW7 2DD

Contents

List of contributors

Joel Bloom	President Emeritus, Franklin Institute Science Museum, Philadelphia
Peter Briggs	Executive Secretary, British Association for the Advancement of Science, London
Bill Brookes	Keeper of Science and Interpretation, Birmingham Museums and Art Gallery
Sylvia Chaplin	Manager, Jodrell Bank Science Centre, Cheshire
John Durant	Assistant Director, Research and Information Services Division, Science Museum, London
Graham Farmelo	Head, Interpretation and Education, Science Museum, London
Dominique Ferriot	Director, Musée National des Techniques, Paris
Francis Graham-Smith	Professor Emeritus, University of Manchester
Patrick Greene	Director, Museum of Science and Industry in Manchester
Willem Hackmann	Acting Curator, Museum of the History of Science, Oxford
Janet Hill	Upper School Co-ordinator, Haycliffe School, near Bradford
Duncan Jackson	Manager, Public Relations Department, Sellafield
Gaynor Kavanagh	Lecturer, Department of Museum Studies, University of Leicester
Roger Miles	Head, Public Services Department, Natural History Museum, London
Gaby Porter	Curatorial Services Manager, Museum of Science and Industry in Manchester
Joël de Rosnay	Director, Development and International Relations, Cité des Sciences et de l'Industrie, Paris
Roger Silverstone	Professor, Department of Media Studies, University of Sussex, Brighton
Patrick Sudbury	Assistant Director (Central Services), National Museums and Galleries on Merseyside
Gillian Thomas	Director, Eureka! The Children's Museum, Halifax
Norman Tomlin	Principal Education Officer, Tyne and Wear Museums Service, Newcastle
Alan Tout	Museum Consultant, Natural History Museum, London
Leonard Will	Head, Science Museum Library, London

Introduction

John Durant

As long as we live, and whatever fate may have been assigned to us, or we have chosen, there is no doubt that the better the quality of our communication, the more useful (and agreeable) to ourselves and others we will be and the longer we will be remembered. He who does not know how to communicate, or communicates badly, in a code that belongs only to him or a few others, is unhappy, and spreads unhappiness around him. If he communicates badly deliberately, he is a wicked or at least a discourteous person, because he imposes labour, anguish, or boredom on his readers.[1]

Primo Levi

The public understanding of science is a catch-phrase that has come to stand for concern about the relationship between science and technology, on the one hand, and the general public, on the other. Over the past decade, such concern has been apparent right across the industrialised world. In Britain, it was signalled by the establishment of a Royal Society working party in the early 1980s. The working party's report appeared in 1985,[2] and it heralded a number of concrete initiatives, including the creation of a research programme with funding from the Economic and Social Research Council, and the establishment of a Committee on the Public Understanding of Science (COPUS). COPUS exists to provide a focus for a broad programme of activities aimed at improving public awareness and understanding of science in the UK. Today, this programme includes: a media fellowship scheme linking scientists and journalists; a Westminster fellowship scheme linking scientists and parliamentarians; the Michael Faraday Award, given annually to the active scientist who has done most to promote the public understanding of science; and (in collaboration with the Science Museum and, more recently, with the assistance of Rhône-Poulenc Ltd) the Science Book Prizes, given annually for the popular science books that have done most to promote the public understanding of science in the UK.

In the late 1980s, COPUS set up a number of working groups on key areas of opportunity within the public understanding of science movement. One of these working groups was concerned with interactive or hands-on science. Chaired by Richard Gregory, the founder of the Bristol Exploratory, this working group encouraged the continued growth of what was already a rapidly expanding network of interactive science centres in the UK. In 1989 it produced a volume of discussion papers entitled *Sharing Science*.[3] Naturally enough, *Sharing Science* was concerned principally with the problems and prospects of a new generation of (mostly independent) science centres. The volume had little to say about the role of museums – apart, that is, from one critical comment by Richard Gregory himself, to which I shall refer later. As a result, COPUS decided to convene a second working group to look specifically at the role of museums in promoting greater public awareness and understanding of science. The COPUS museums working group was set up in the autumn of 1990. Its remit includes both specialist science and technology museums and general museums which devote part of their exhibition space to science (including medical science and natural history) and/or technology.

Early in the deliberations of the museums working group, it was decided to convene an international conference to explore key issues with colleagues, to take place in the Science Museum, London, on 8 and 9 April 1992. In preparation for the conference, and in order to forward the working group's deliberations, discussion papers were commissioned from working group members and from museologists working in Britain, other western European countries, and north America. The present volume brings these papers together, and it is offered both as a pre-conference publication and as a contribution to the wider international debate about the role of museums in promoting the public understanding of science.

What is the distinctive role of museums in relation to the public understanding of science? This question may be addressed by returning for a moment to the comparison between interactive science centres and science museums. Clearly, these two types of institution have a great deal in common with one another. Both are places visited by the general public; both provide exhibits designed to inform visitors about science; and both attempt to inform at least in part by inviting visitors to explore phenomena with the help of interactive demonstrations and experiments. Certainly, the science centre movement has come a long way over the past decade, but its rapid growth should not blind us to the fact that it has close ties to the pre-existing world of science museums. This fact is most obvious in those cases – such as *Launch Pad* in the Science Museum, London, and *Xperiment!* in the Manchester Museum of Science and Industry – where interactive science centres are actually housed inside museums.

Having emphasised the close links that exist between science centres and science museums, it is important to acknowledge that there are also many differences between them. At the risk of a good deal of over-generalisation, I should like to contrast what science centres and science museums offer to the public. Generally speaking, a science centre comprises one or more relatively open spaces in which are located a large number of free-standing interactive exhibits, whereas a science museum comprises several relatively closed spaces in which are located a small number of permanent or temporary exhibitions. Typically, a science centre interactive is a device that embodies an elementary scientific or technological principle, and visitors are encouraged to 'play' with this device, usually with a minimum of textual or other guidance, in order to 'discover' the principle for themselves. A science museum exhibition is a scripted 'story' about an entire area of science or technology, told with the assistance of many different objects, interactives, captions, and (increasingly) audio-visual and electronic media.

Casting caution to the winds, we might say that a science centre presents a smorgasbord of bite-sized chunks of science, whereas a science museum presents a menu of more or less carefully concocted scientific dishes. Each type of offering has characteristic strengths and weaknesses. Thus, the science centre smorgasbord is ambitious both in its attempt to convey something of the spirit of scientific inquiry and in its concern to instill what Richard Gregory calls a 'hand-waving' grasp of basic scientific principles, but it tends to present a fragmented and decontextualised picture of science. Many science centres arrange their interactives in clusters by subject such as light, or flight. However, most of those with which I am familiar make little attempt to convey any sort of systematic understanding at a level beyond that at which individual interactives are designed to operate. For this reason above all, it is hard to see how interactive science alone (at least as we know it today) can be much more than an appetizer (or perhaps an *hors d'oeuvre?*), preparing the way for more substantial fare in the world of science education.

Similarly, the science museum menu is ambitious in its attempt to convey a sense of the nature or the development of an entire field of science or technology, often through very long periods of time, but it tends to neglect the principles and processes of science in favour of the celebration of concrete (often technological) achievements. A typical science museum exhibition might consist of an historical survey of progress in a particular field of practical scientific endeavour. Almost certainly, such an exhibition will attempt to compress a great deal of complex material into a relatively small space, and, as often as not, the result will be a series of intended messages many or even most of which are inaccessible to all but the most committed and well-prepared visitors. Still today, as Gaynor Kavanagh's contribution to this volume makes abundantly clear, it is important for those of us who work in science museums to acknowledge that many of our exhibitions are open to Primo Levi's accusation that they spread unhappiness around them by communicating badly.

The differences between science centres and science museums are rooted firmly in the single distinction between the two types of institution which deserves to be termed fundamental: science centres do not hold collections of scientific artefacts (instruments, tools, equipment, etc) for the benefit of posterity, and science museums do. Generally speaking, science centres exist for but a single basic purpose: to promote public understanding of science through exhibitions and associated programmes. By contrast, science museums exist for two basic purposes: to hold scientific collections, and to promote public understanding of science through exhibitions and associated programmes. (It should be noted in passing that of course natural history museums contain collections of natural objects – rocks, plants, animals – rather than artefacts; these impose different, but equally severe, constraints upon natural history exhibitions.)

More than anything else, it is the collections-based view of science that is responsible for the characteristic preoccupations of science museum exhibitions. These exhibitions dwell on the past more than the present because for the most part collections have been amassed over decades or centuries, and of necessity they have become of principally historical interest. They dwell on the practical more than the theoretical because for the most part artefacts lend themselves to the illustration of technical achievements (the harnessing of power, the development of land transport, the conquest of space) more readily than to the illustration of fundamental scientific ideas or theories (the laws of thermodynamics, the principles of mechanics, the relativistic conception of space-time). Admittedly, it is possible to convey something of the basic principles of early cosmology with the help of orreries and telescopes, but any attempt to do the same with Einsteinian physics, or molecular biology, is more or less doomed to failure. If we are honest, we must admit that this is because as often as not the artefacts of twentieth-century science are both mind-bogglingly dull and utterly uninformative to behold.

The purpose of this contrast between science centres and science museums is to indicate that each has come to specialise in a characteristic type of science communication. Well executed, each type of communication is valid in its own terms and has something to contribute to the public understanding of science. In this sense, therefore, I disagree with some of the criticisms that exponents of interactive science tend to level at science museums. According to Richard Gregory, for example, 'it is remarkable how little science there is in traditional science museums'.[4] In fact, there is a great deal of science (in the broadest sense) in science museums; but, as I have tried to show, it is a type of science quite different from that to be found in science centres. In a nutshell, museums tend to specialise in that part of science which may be encountered through the history of striking technical achievement, whereas science centres tend to specialise in that part of science which may be encountered through the personal experience of striking natural phenomena. Potentially, each is an authentic representation of part, but only part, of the world of science.

To some extent, science centre and science museum approaches are complementary; indeed, there are clear signs of convergence between the two. As I have already indicated, most science museums have long recognised the value of interactive exhibits within themed exhibitions. At the same time, it appears that many science centres are beginning to recognise the value of themed exhibitions. This convergence upon the notion of highly interactive exhibitions is to be welcomed. Taken to the limit, it will blur the distinction between science centres and science museums. Indeed, should science centres fall prey to the seduction of acquiring genuine scientific apparatus for the purpose of developing more authentic interactive exhibits, then of necessity they will find themselves gradually turning into science museums. Whether or not this ultimate convergence takes place, however, science museums will still be left with a number of unresolved issues, among which I suggest that three are particularly important: the museum as medium; the museum as message; and the museum as educational resource.

First, in spite of the comparatively long history of science museums, the harsh reality is that the art of exhibiting science to the public is still in its infancy. In part, this is because we have been slow to come to terms with the true nature of the museum as a communicative medium. Two clear messages contained in this volume are that museums are distinct media for the dissemination of messages about science, and that museum visitors are not just one, but several distinct audiences for those messages. Only very recently have museums taken up the challenge of finding out what sorts of people come through their doors, and (of equal or even greater importance) what sorts of things these people do once they are safely inside. Such empirical work as has been done suggests that in the past a great deal of museum time and money has been spent unprofitably, for want of any adequately realistic sense of what audiences can be expected either to attend to or to assimilate in the course of a single visit.

If coming to terms with the nature of museums and museum audiences is one part of the secret of building successful science exhibitions, another is surely coming to terms with the nature of exhibitions themselves. Here, as Joël de Rosnay suggests, the key question is: how should exhibitions deal with complexity? Science is the paradigm of complex, relatively inaccessible knowledge. Journalists, broadcasters and others have developed many different skills appropriate to the conveying of such complexity through their own chosen media. The challenge facing those of us who work in museums is to match these skills with others that are equally well-suited to exhibitions. As Rosnay points out, it is a matter not only of making exhibition messages clear but also of making them multiply accessible, both physically (ie, from wherever the visitor chooses to start) and intellectually (ie, from whatever level of engagement or prior expertise the visitor happens to possess). Science museums need to cultivate interpretive skills of a high order if they are to meet the challenges posed by the complexity of their subject matter.

Second, there is the question of the messages about science that museums are concerned to convey. Here, I am struck by a curious shared weakness in the otherwise rather different contents of science centres and science museums. For both types of institution have a tendency to represent science in a way that divorces it from social reality. The image of science that I find in most science centres is one of clear, elementary principles wait-ing to be discovered by anyone with sufficient child-like curiosity and adult patience to search them out. By contrast, the image of science that I find in most science museums (including, it should be said, large parts of my own) is one of sure and solid progress in the mastery of nature. In both cases, science itself emerges as a fixed body of knowledge and practice, more or less totally be-yond either doubt or dispute, and in both cases, two relevant social groups are strangely absent: first, the authors of all these achievements, scien-tists themselves; and second, the wider culture within which these people pursue their work.

The presentation of science as a fixed body of knowledge and the presentation of science divorced from its immediate social context are surely con-nected. For of course it is in the social world of real scientists engaging with one another in their work that scientific consensus is generally achieved. To be fair to us all, our museums do introduce scientists into exhibitions fairly frequent-ly, but all too often these people are presented as archetypal lonely geniuses. Only rarely (as was the case in our recent bicentennial exhibition: *Making the Difference: Charles Babbage and the Birth of the Computer*) do museum exhibitions manage to set scientists so firmly within their professional and social worlds that visitors can begin to see how

new scientific knowledge is actually produced.[5] In my view, museums should strive to find new and more effective ways of portraying science in the making. For only in this way can we be true both to the nature of science itself and to the needs of a general public which is continuously exposed to new (and often conflicting) scientific knowledge claims in the mass media.[6]

One way of portraying science in the making is through genuinely contextual historical exhibitions; but another is through exhibitions that deal with contemporary scientific ideas and issues. As we have seen, science museum exhibitions tend to concentrate on the past but there is no reason why they should not deal with the present (and even the future as well). In the Science Museum, for example, we have recently instituted a *Contempo-rary Science* exhibition programme. The aim is to mount a series of three or four small, topical exhibitions per year. The first exhibition is due to open in spring 1992 and will deal with genetic fingerprinting. By being topical, contemporary science exhibitions have the potential to convey the difficulties, the doubts, and the uncertainties fre-quently associated with real science; indeed, as Roger Silverstone suggests in his contribution to this volume, they can even comment upon the role of other media in constructing and/or commenting upon scientific issues in the public domain.

The third and last set of issues with which we have to deal concern the museum as educational resource. Museum visitor studies have a tendency to induce gloom in museum interpreters by reveal-ing how rapidly most people pass through exhibi-tions, and how rarely they stop to pay close atten-tion to anything in particular. Arguably, the antidote to such gloom is equal parts of better exhibition interpretation and better educational resource. By educational resource, I mean all of the programming elements that museums provide in addition to the exhibitions themselves. Such re-source includes interpretive staff (actors, explain-ers, guides), written materials (information packs, guidebooks, teachers' guides), films, videos, lec-tures, demonstrations, and other information services aimed at audiences both inside and outside the museum. In recent years, science museums have shown a welcome enthusiasm for the deploy-ment of new educational resources to complement exhibition programmes, but of course there is still a great deal more that can and should be done.

One trend that is evident in educational

programming in both science centres and science museums is the increasing use of people to back up interactives and exhibitions. Although interactives are central to the work of science centres, most now employ interpreters (variously described as guides, explainers, pilots, etc) to help visitors make sense of their experiences, and an increasing number feature regular floor shows in which staff interpret a particular area of science or technology by means of practical demonstrations. Here, again, there is a clear convergence between science centres and science museums, for museums too are becoming living places that feature people alongside objects and displays. Gallery tours, demonstrations, and lectures all have an important place in science museum educational programming, and, as Graham Farmelo reports in his contribution to this volume, gallery drama has proved a huge success almost everywhere that it has been tried. However good science museums become at interpreting science through exhibitions, they need to remember that even the best inanimate display can literally be brought to life by the addition of personal interpretation.

The essays in this volume are organised thematically. The first essay by Joel Bloom of the Franklin Institute Science Museum in Philadelphia sets the scene by reviewing the present position and future potential of science museums as educational and cultural resources. The next section is devoted to the role of museum exhibitions. Joël de Rosnay analyses how exhibitions deal with complex material; Roger Miles and Alan Tout review exhibition visitor studies; and Roger Silverstone reflects on the distinctive characteristics of museum exhibitions. The third section is concerned with museum programmes. Graham Farmelo, Leonard Will, Janet Hill, Patrick Sudbury, Willem Hackmann, Peter Briggs, and Norman Tomlin report on the strengths and weaknesses of different museum programmes, ranging from gallery drama to the Boston Museum's innovative experiment with *Science-by-mail*. There is a great deal to be learnt from the programmes described here, and I hope readers will be stimulated to borrow and adapt ideas for their own purposes.

Museums have their own individual characteristics, rooted in history and context, and these individual characteristics provide individual opportunities for excellence. The fourth section deals with concrete museum experiences. Dominique Ferriot, Gaynor Kavanagh, Gillian Thomas, Patrick Greene and Gaby Porter, and Bill Brookes report on work currently being done in particular museums. Finally, in an attempt to prevent ourselves from being too parochial, we have invited contributions from people who run visitor centres in scientific and technological institutions rather than museums. Duncan Jackson reports on the much publicised Sellafield Visitors' Centre in Cumbria, and Sylvia Chaplin and Francis Graham-Smith describe the work of the Jodrell Bank Visitor Centre.

Science museums share with science centres and visitor centres in major research laboratories the marvellous opportunity to share science with the interested general public. Uniquely, science museums bring to this sharing exercise the rich resource of their historic collections, which open windows onto the history of science and technology, and thus (quite literally) onto the making of our modern world. I doubt whether there has ever been a time in the history of science museums when there has been as much reconsideration of responsibility and renewal and redirection of effort as there is today. This volume, and the international conference at the Science Museum with which it is linked, are intended to clarify our thinking and to sharpen our resolve that science museums shall be even more relevant to the interests and needs of the general public in the future than they have been in the past.

Notes and references

1 Levi, P, *Other People's Trades* (London: Michael Joseph, 1989) p162

2 *The Public Understanding of Science* (London: Royal Society, 1985)

3 *Sharing Science* (London: Nuffield Foundation, 1989)

4 *Sharing Science*, p2

5 See Swade, D, *Charles Babbage and His Calculating Engines* (London: Science Museum, 1991)

6 See Shapin, S, 'Why the public ought to understand science-in-the-making', *Public Understanding of Science*, 1 (1992), pp27-30

Looking forward

Science and technology museums face the future

Joel Bloom

At the end of the last century, people were dazzled by the wonders of science and technology. The theme parks of the day were industrial expositions showcasing the steam engines and other mechanical marvels that were both the symbols and the reality of progress. Indeed, the great science museums in London and Munich may be traced to these expositions. Man was master of all he surveyed, destined to rule the world and all it contained. We gloried in our conquest of nature. As this century draws to a close, science and technology continue to offer exciting new possibilities. Computers become more powerful, more accessible and less expensive every day. We continually gain new insights into the human body and its functions, learn new ways to diagnose, treat, and prevent illness. New transportation systems are being developed. Today, prototype magnetically levitated trains speed passengers across Germany and Japan at 250 miles per hour. Scientists are even working to decipher the human genetic code, a project that will lead to a far greater understanding of the mechanics of genetic diseases and may someday permit us to prevent or even cure them.

Yet with all these wonders, our enthusiasm for science and technology has tarnished. Perhaps our love affair with the wonders of modern science started to fade when the *Enola Gay* dropped the first atomic bomb on Hiroshima. Perhaps it was 15 years later, with the publication of *Silent Spring* and the alarm it raised about the effects of insecticides on the ecosystem, a word which had not been invented for a concept that was only beginning to be understood.

Today, we are increasingly aware of our relationship to our planet. We are beginning to understand that like all living things, we are dependent on our world, not its unchallenged masters. We may indeed have appeared to conquer nature, but we find little glory in this accomplishment. Newspapers and magazines are filled with apocalyptic, perhaps exaggerated visions of a parched greenhouse world, seared by ultraviolet rays that pierce a depleted ozone layer, its air and water poisoned by toxic chemicals. Will these dark visions come to pass? For all our scientific achievements, we do not know. There are those who question whether we should have eaten from the Tree of Knowledge. Be that as it may, the gates to the Garden of Eden are most assuredly barred. We cannot return to a simpler, non-technological existence, and few of us would choose to live without antibiotics, indoor plumbing, or telecommunications.

By the beginning of the next century, six billion people will inhabit this planet, sharing it with millions of species of plants and animals. Our planet is finite. Its limited resources can only support its inhabitants if we learn to make better use of the awesome power our knowledge has provided. Otherwise, the apocalyptic visions of the future may truly come to pass.

It is increasingly clear that humankind must make the future a matter of 'choice not chance'. What kinds of choices must we make if we are to choose our future? In the Los Angeles basin, an ambitious plan has been developed to balance environmental protection and economic development in a region notorious for atmospheric pollution. The recent Montreal Accord, an agreement to limit global production of chlorofluorocarbons, is an attempt to respond rationally to a difficult issue. In Philadelphia, an experimental first phase of a broad-based recycling program has achieved an unprecedented 80 per cent participation rate. Here too, people are choosing their future, and contributing to a rational solution of the problem of solid waste disposal. Examples from other countries are legion.

Ultimately, we must look beyond such specific issues, beyond the important, indeed, seemingly miraculous, discoveries that will no doubt emerge from the laboratories of the twenty-first century. Knowledge is the most powerful tool we, the toolmakers, have ever invented. Our knowledge of science and technology has shaped our world, for good and for ill. Although it has created problems, it has also helped us understand these problems, and without it we cannot develop long-term solutions.

Now, we must grow in wisdom. For the first time in history, we have the power to destroy our world, as well as the power to make real the age-old dream of a just and humane world. Which future will we choose? For our profession, what role will museums, especially science and technology museums, play at this critical juncture in human history?

Clearly ecological issues know no national boundaries. In like manner, although the specifics in this paper are mostly couched in US terms, the basic ideas apply world wide. I shall be commenting on education and the public understanding of science. These are matters of vital concern not only to us as museum professionals, but to all humankind.

In the early 1980s I had the honor to serve as co-chair of the American Association of Museums' Commission on Museums for a New Century. The Commission was charged with identifying the forces of change which are shaping the future for America's museums. We then looked at the ramifications of these forces, both internal and external. We identified an upheaval in the American educational system as one of the major forces of change, and emphasised the importance of education in the mission of America's museums. Today, I would, of course, add the world's museums.

In September 1989, it was my privilege, as President of the American Association of Museums, to appoint a task force on museum education. The group was ably chaired by Bonnie Pitman, Deputy Director of the University Art Museum, University of California, Berkeley. Let me quote from the letter of invitation to the distinguished members of this task force:

> As you know, the museum community has long been concerned with education. Many institutions have education as a basic element in their charters, and some in fact see education as their primary reason for existence.

The report of the Commission on Museums for a New Century cogently described the role of education in our nation's museums in the following way:

> Many consider public education to be the most significant contribution this country has made to the evolution of the museum concept ... if collections are the heart of museums, what we have come to call

education – the commitment to presenting objects and ideas in an informative and stimulating manner – is the spirit.

Some two dozen people were invited to serve on the task force. They came from museums of all sizes and disciplines as well as the world of foundations and academe. Their charge was to develop a report on the issues and needs of the museum field concerning education and the role the American Association of Museums might play in addressing these needs. Again, the issues are global and the British term Museums Association would, perhaps, be more appropriate. The first meeting of the task force revealed some significant differences of opinion regarding museum education: what it is, what it should be. Some of the divisions were, as one might expect, a matter of museum discipline. Others were more complex.

The fact is that once we move beyond truisms, education becomes a very tricky issue, and consensus difficult to attain. Even within the field, there are conflicts of opinion about the relationship between preservation and interpretation, between collections and education. The very word education can mean different things to different people. As a result, what seems to be agreement can vanish when we seek to define our terms.

Given the complexity of the issues involved, why venture into these murky waters? Because literally nothing is more important. Our future as a species depends on the decisions we make about how to educate our children to face the challenges of the next century. The late Frank Oppenheimer, founder and director of the Exploratorium, said it very well:

> The whole point of education is to transmit culture, and museums can play an increasingly important role in this process. It is a mistake to think that preserving culture is distinct from transmitting it through education.

Today more and more museums define themselves as educational institutions. At the risk of seeming parochial I believe this to be one of the fundamental contributions Americans have made to the development of museums. I suspect, however, that the nineteenth-century pioneers of American museums had a very different definition of education than that which is developing today. To them education meant that the public should be educated on the museum's terms, on the museum's turf. In those days education usually meant formal programs. In general, the more a museum program was like a school, the more 'educational' it seemed. Let me share a story about my own museum, the Franklin Institute, which was founded in 1824. When our current neo-classical structure was built in 1933, it encompassed vast, grand exhibition halls. As soon as the building was completed, literally half of these great halls were partitioned into classroom-sized rooms. At that time, the Franklin Institute educators believed that a lecture better fulfilled our educational role than an exhibit. Perhaps the staff was seeking respectability among their colleagues in the schools.

At that time, there was very little question about the primacy of mainstream culture. The concept of cultural pluralism did not exict. Museums were temples of culture, islands of serenity in an increasingly industrialised America. The 'city beautiful' concept reigned in city planning, and museums were often placed in parks located on the outskirts of the town. This is a classic example of something that seemed like a good idea at the time. It has not proved advantageous for those museums which are placed outside the heart of their communities.

Today, we place more emphasis on the educational significance of the museum visit. We have developed the new concept of 'informal education' to describe the many ways people learn outside the classroom. Informal education includes reading books and magazines, watching television or movies, observing the natural world, visiting a museum. Still, the old model retains much power, and we ourselves can be defensive about the educational impact of museums. When we say 'museum education', we often refer to classroom experiences in the museum which are structured programs with a teacher and a group of students. Discussions of museum education often flounder on different definitions of the term itself.

Of course, our education departments also offer less formal programs. Some are serious programs for interested amateurs. Others are light-hearted programs to entice the general public to visit us. But how often do we think of such programs when we speak of museum education? This is ironic, for in our hearts, most of us truly believe that the museum visit is educationally significant, both in the affective and the cognitive realms. In fact, many specialists in museum evaluation believe that the affective aspect of museum learning may be more significant than the cognitive.

A museum can inspire visitors to ask questions, to pursue new-found interests on their own. This may well have more long-term impact than the nuggets of information an exhibit can convey. I cannot tell you how many times scientists or engineers have told me that their interest in science was sparked by an early experience at The Franklin Institute. There is also a file of letters from children at the Institute. They often say that a visit changed their minds about science. They thought science was boring. Now, they know it can be fun to learn.

I believe that we must learn how to assess the power of museum education and seriously investigate the way people learn in museums. We should do this both to document our impact and to learn how we can be even more effective.

Very little is known about the dynamics of informal learning. Indeed, less than we would like to admit is known about the dynamics of formal learning. Informal learning, especially the object-based learning that takes place in a museum, has been investigated very little by the academic research establishment. This, I suspect, is because experimental psychologists work largely with rats. Rats have extraordinarily keen senses of smell and hearing. Their ability to appreciate art and to understand history is less highly developed. Since they lack opposed thumbs, they cannot manipulate interactive exhibit devices. Today, museum learning is being formally investigated, often by museums themselves. For example, current research indicates that museum-style object-based learning is particularly effective in countering erroneous beliefs about the physical universe. These so-called naive theories of science are very difficult to eradicate in the classroom setting. Research at the Franklin Institute and other science museums is proving unequivocally that these naive theories can be altered using specially designed interactive exhibit devices. For example, seemingly educated people persist in the belief that gravity somehow requires air to operate. Weightlessness in space, they think, is caused by lack of air. Show these people that gravity works in a vacuum and they understand once and for all. Theoretical knowledge is deepened and enhanced by observed reality.

Research into the dynamics and impact of museum learning will serve another, perhaps parochial purpose as well. Museum professionals often speak of the need to change the perception of museums, to show that we are important to our communities. This is an era of diminishing public funding and increased competition for corporate and foundation support. In the US, and I am certain in other countries, museums compete for funding with programs for the homeless, treatment and prevention of substance abuse, teenage pregnancy, high-school drop-outs. Education is widely accepted as an important part of solutions to pressing problems. As legitimate educational institutions we are better situated to make a successful case for support, be it public or private sector.

What is unique about education in the museum setting? A museum offers direct, one-to-one, personal experience, the chance to experience real objects. Even in this media-saturated 'information age', there is no substitute for the power of reality.

A museum visit is self-structured. There are no performance standards. No one can fail a museum visit. Our visitors are free to explore without fear of failure; to return again and again to something that interests them. I believe absolutely that a museum is a place of learning. It is a special place where people can follow their own interests; browse until they find something that inspires more focused attention and perhaps lights a spark that burns for a lifetime.

All this is important. But it is not enough. In recent years, as public concern about the state of education in America grows, museums are more and more taking the initiative. They are playing a more active role in our communities. They form broad-based partnerships to address educational issues. They work with school systems and the corporate community to improve public education. Because museums are experts in teaching voluntary learners they introduce a unique perspective into educational planning. Although they are educational institutions, they compete in the crowded leisure time marketplace. Museums must make learning enjoyable for their visitors. Their experience can serve as models for formal education, as well.

I believe that in the future, partnerships between schools and museums will flourish and grow. I also believe that museums will provide more and more opportunities for the adult learner. The 'shelf-life' of an education is getting shorter. Career change is becoming the norm rather than the exception. As a result, lifelong learning will become more and more important. In the US today, adult participation in education is growing. More than one-third of the students enrolled in higher education institutions are adults. In fact, education is one of the most popular ways to use discretionary time.

Museums have an important role to play in this new educational environment. This includes expanding our informal educational offerings. We can work more closely with the schools and provide professional development opportunities to educators. I also suspect that we may find ourselves involved in a new educational area. As I said, there is increasing concern about the quality of American education. Often, corporations find it difficult to recruit qualified workers. As a result, many businesses are becoming directly involved in education, providing professional development for senior staff or remedial education for entry-level workers. This may offer a new opportunity for museums. I believe that it is impossible to overstate the importance of museum involvement in education at every level, for every age group.

As museums deepen their involvement in education, they will increasingly confront another set of challenges. Yes, we are educational institutions. Whom are we educating? What are we teaching? How should we make these decisions?

This is not a simple question. It relates to complex social factors that are shaping the future for us all and cannot be neatly separated from educational issues. Two inter-related forces of societal change are involved. The first is our growing recognition and acceptance of cultural diversity. It is tempting to suggest that this is, perhaps, a uniquely American problem, stemming from our multi-ethnic, multiracial, multicultural society. Recent events in the former Soviet Union, Yugoslavia, and indeed in the birthpangs of the European Community, suggest otherwise. Once, the American cultural ideal was the melting pot. We wanted to lose our old world identities and create a new, American identity. We no longer aspire to the melting pot. We celebrate our diversity. We do not try to submerge it.

America is becoming a nation of minorities. More than half of US population growth in this century will take place in minority communities. About 25 per cent of our population growth is the result of immigration. By the year 2030, 20 per cent of our population will be of African, Asian or Hispanic origin. The proliferation of ethnic restaurants demonstrates this trend, as do the explosive popularity of 'world-beat' music and the growth of media in languages other than English. Increasingly we recognise and accept the cultural pluralism of our society as a distinctive element in our national character. It should be reflected in all our institutions, including, of course, museums.

A second powerful force has equally profound implications for museums. It is a new kind of populism: a proliferation of voices that has resulted in a fundamental change in the decision-making process. It is inextricably intertwined with the growing acceptance of a multicultural America. Here, too, I speak of the American experience, but am quite certain that in our evolving global society, the issue is also applicable to much of the rest of the world. Decisions can no longer be handed down from the top. Traditional hierarchical structures are being modified. Many more players demand a role. In the workplace and in society as a whole, there is a broader base of participation. Growing evidence for this new style of decision making comes from the growth of special interest politics, the move to new management styles, the search for 'win-win' conflict resolution in which no one loses. Every voice believes it has a right to be heard. A Midwestern American housewife is offended by the language and subject matter of a television program. Not too long ago, she would have changed the channel and forgotten about it. Today, she begins a campaign that leads to the cancellation of half the advertising on the offending show.

The confluence of these two forces of change has profound implications for museums. One of the most obvious expressions is the growth of ethnic museums and arts centres. In Philadelphia, for example, we have a Swedish-American Museum, an Afro-American Museum, a National Museum of American Jewish History, a Puerto Rican Arts Centre, and the Balch Institute for Ethnic Studies. But such specialty museums are only the beginning. Many American museums are hearing the voices of a pluralistic community and are developing programs and exhibits to serve their needs. But the fact is that the traditional mainstream culture continues to pervade our museums.

If you ask 'why not?', just talk to the Native Americans (American Indians) who are fighting to rescue what they believe to be their cultural heritage and their ancestors' very bones. Listen to the words of women and minority artists, who believe that they have been systematically, if unconsciously, excluded from the mainstream.

There is no such thing as a neutral museum exhibit. An exhibit is the result of myriad decisions, large and small. Museums are widely perceived as arbiters of culture, touchstones of quality. The decisions we make will be scrutinised closely by the mainstream and by the vocal minorities holding more extreme positions.

These are not simple issues. It will be difficult indeed to forge a compromise between Native Americans and the legitimate scholarly concerns of anthropologists and archaeologists. It is difficult to give proper weight to the historical primacy of the mainstream as well as the cultural significance of the disenfranchised. Regrettably, such conflicts often become political fighting grounds, and resolution becomes yet more difficult. No decision can satisfy all the stakeholders. Further controversy seems inevitable. How can we juggle these apparently irreconcilable demands? How do we decide what we include and what we leave out? Whose side of the story should history museums tell? Who has the 'true' right to the Elgin Marbles (as if there were a singular 'truth')? Who decides? What criteria do we use?

Anthropological museums are wrestling with these issues when they decide how to present tribal culture. Many ethnographic museum exhibits edit. They collect the contents of a village in Papua New Guinea. Then they eliminate everything that does not look authentic, even if it really is authentic. These days, most native villages in Papua New Guinea contain tin cans, World War II surplus gear, factory-woven cotton cloth, plastic jugs. Is it more authentic to remove these seemingly incongruous objects? or to present the village as it really is?

What standards do we use when we select artefacts for our exhibits? What cultural biases shape our criteria? We can confidently anticipate a great deal of heat over this question during the forthcoming Columbus Quincentenary, the 500th anniversary of Columbus' first voyage to the Caribbean. It is defined as a celebration, yet Native Americans passionately protest that they have nothing to celebrate. They see Columbus as a genocidal conqueror who 'discovered' their homeland. Italian Americans see him quite differently.

The educational community has been wrestling with such issues for some time. Are standardised tests a fair assessment of intellectual potential? Do they confer an unfair advantage on middle-class students? How should American history be taught? What about black history? What literature belongs in the English curriculum? Again, the questions are cast in American terms, but analogous issues can be found in almost every corner of the world.

The proliferation of voices and the recognition of diversity have resulted in a politicisation of education. Ironically, this has resulted in a retreat from controversy, not a balanced exploration of opposing views. A perfect example is the controversy over Mark Twain's *Huckleberry Finn*. This American masterpiece has been castigated for racism. After all, one of the main characters bears the name Nigger Jim, which is totally unacceptable today. Yet if we look beyond that word, we find a powerful case for human equality, and a very readable story as well.

Today, many educators deplore the blandness of their textbooks. Publishers prefer to avoid offense. No matter how balanced the treatment of a difficult issue, extremists are likely to object. Extremists do not search for balance. They generally demand complete agreement with their positions. Unfortunately, it seems that something that is designed to offend no one, is unlikely to interest anyone. The Columbus controversy is an example of this same politicisation in the world of museums. It doee not foreshadow a simple future. As a community, we are moving towards a stronger definition of museums as educational institutions. If we expand this role as such, and I believe we must, we will be subject to increasing pressure from diverse communities. Communities will expect to be represented in our institutions, to participate in our decisions. Inevitably, there will be objections to some of these decisions. It would be tragic indeed if we too retreated from controversy and opted only for the safe, the sanitised.

Let me share a story from my childhood. I spent many Saturdays visiting New York's museums, and was profoundly affected by Picasso's *Guernica* at the Museum of Modern Art. As a child, I understood little about the events that it depicts. I knew nothing about Cubism or contemporary painting. Nevertheless, it spoke to me on a deep emotional level. My instinctive response to that painting helped shape deeply felt beliefs about justice and human rights that persist to this day.

We cannot underestimate the impact we may have. We must not forget that the child who stands silent before *Guernica* may grow up to be a somewhat different adult. An Anselm Kiefer painting is among the most powerful arguments against another Holocaust. Iron slave chains may teach more about black America than any textbook.

The politicisation of culture has already begun: in the controversy over the repatriation of Native American remains and artefacts; the recent addition of slave quarters at Colonial Williamsburg; the demands made by African Americans that their lost heroes be included in history and science museum exhibits. More problematical are the demands by evangelical Christians that 'creation science' be included in Earth science and palaeontology exhibits and in planetarium shows.

Our society likes answers. Uncertainty is difficult for us to accept. Yet we must learn to live with it. Beneath the issues of cultural diversity and what I have called the new populism are fundamental questions, questions about our very nature as human beings. Education raises these questions because education is how culture is transmitted. By tackling the issue of museum education – what it is and what it should be – we have undertaken a difficult task. Still, we must continue to ask these questions. We may never agree on the answers. As museums move into an ever more complex, option-filled future, we can serve society by providing a place to explore these issues.

The future will not be a simple place in which to live, yet we will spend the rest of our lives there. No matter how complicated the world becomes, I believe that there will always be a place for museums; for the special kind of learning that takes place in museums; for the special role we can play in meeting the educational demands of future citizens.

The role of the museum

Intellectual ergonomics and multimedia exhibitions

Joël de Rosnay

The providing of training and information in modern societies requires the transfer of knowledge in the form of interdependent messages, signs, codes and symbols. These messages are addressed to varying publics and represent different levels of abstraction. The traditional methods of support complement one another to reinforce certain aspects of communications: books, graphics, photos, slides, videos, films, interactive software – all are used in varying degrees and with their own specific features to put across the elements which are essential for the acquisition of knowledge. In this panoply of didactic and pedagogic media, aimed at increasing our sensitivities and deepening our awareness, the multimedia exhibition has a particular role to fulfil. This type of exhibition is capable of integrating, in the same spatial area, panels comprising text, photographs, drawings and graphics, audio-visual presentations, mock-ups, and interactive equipment ranging from the simple computer simulation game to the most complex of mechanical or electronic devices. Often expensive, these exhibitions are nevertheless becoming more and more lavish and widespread, as likely to be found in the dignified chambers of professional institutions as they are in artistic, scientific, technical or industrial centres.

It might, however, be asked how effective these exhibitions are, given the wealth of modern communications systems available. What is their specific contribution, and how do they complement other support media such as books, courses, conferences, television broadcasts, or simulation software? How will they need to develop in the future in order to integrate the complexity of the messages to be put across? And, above all, how should we best make use of them in order to allow visitors to derive maximum benefit from the presentations provided as part of a personalised encounter? These questions give rise to a new approach to the exhibition, considering it as an integrated system of communications capable of providing a system of tailor-made interfaces.

The first scientific and technical exhibitions were inspired by encyclopaedias. What was involved then was, primarily, putting up texts and photographs on stands, backed up by mock-ups of real objects: instruments, machines, or heavy equipment, witnesses to technical development. Architects and scenographers were asked to 'dress' a space, to provide it with a coherence and a style likely to attract a visitor's attention and to keep them on the spot. The person who mounted the exhibition became literally a 'producer' in spatial terms, much as we might speak of a 'producer' in terms of scenery in the theatre or cinema, having in this context responsibility for and control of the quality of the content of the messages intended for the visitors. This style of exhibition, in the form of a 'book on the walls' has steadily given way, thanks to technical progress, to interactive exhibitions in which audio-visual techniques, the computer, the video disk, animated screens, and sketches performed by robotised figures play an ever more important role. Visitors are no longer content simply to read texts or watch audio-visuals; they want to participate in experiences, do something active, answer questions, initiate new sequences of interactive encounters. This means that exhibition planners too have steadily developed, sometimes without being aware of it, into 'systems engineers' in multimedia communications. Undoubtedly, scenographers, designers, and graphic artists have continued to play their part, but conflicts have arisen between museographic designers and animators over styles or methods of spatial implementation, giving preference to the form as a spectacle over the actual content of the messages.

Three types of exhibition could be described today in which the new communications technologies are used on a broad scale. The first is the 'linear' exhibition, which presents a subject in a sequential manner, dividing it arbitrarily into periods (such as chronological sequences), into disciplines, or even by following a didactic progression from the 'simple' to the 'complex'. The second is the 'matrix' exhibition, in which no sequence as such is imposed, but rather juxtaposed sectors are presented, the interactive elements of which are located at the points of intersection of the visitor's encounter. The third is the 'discovery' exhibition, a kind of labyrinth of knowledge intended to stimulate the visitor's curiosity by presenting some element which attracts the attention as the visitor passes down the aisle, and arouses a desire to find out more.

Regrettably, these three types of exhibition only partially meet the constraints imposed by the complexity of the messages and their contents. If the elements of the museographic presentations are too detailed, there is a risk of losing the guiding thread of the whole. An exhibition which is overly analytical no longer summons up a vision of synthesis. Conversely, an approach which is too general deprives visitors of the precise details which inspire them to set their imagination to work and increase the depth of their knowledge. Added to these disadvantages are the frequent restrictions imposed by the space itself, with a surfeit of information resulting from the close juxtaposition of texts with photographs, audio-visuals, or interactive processes, which are difficult to understand. The lack of hierarchy among the themes and sub-themes and the weakness of the descriptions renders the organisation of the messages still more confused.

It seems to me, therefore, that we have a need to go beyond the architectural vision alone, or the scenographic or graphic representation of a multimedia exhibition, in order to consider the relationship with the visitor (reader/spectator/active participant), in the 'system of communications', and no longer think only of the 'communication space'. As with every interactive system, and every machine or computer with a direct interface to one or more users, we are therefore led to define and implement at an exhibition what I shall call from now on 'intellectual ergonomics'. This involves a methodological and technical approach which is intended to favour the acquisition of knowledge by providing an adequate relationship between objects and subjects, by the simplicity of the methods of use, and by the ease and comfort of the user/machine interfaces. For a computer, these ergonomics are translated into reality in part by the notion of user-friendliness. For a machine, office equipment, or a work station in a design studio, well-designed ergonomics will allow for improvements in the efficiency of interrelations between user, tools, and equipment. An instrument panel, a receiver unit, or a control system will therefore possess a type of ergonomics more or less well-adapted to the needs of their users.

From now on, it will be appropriate to create multimedia interactive exhibitions by integrating intellectual ergonomics into the museographic entity. The exhibition as an entity must therefore be conceived and used as one single interactive system (and not only as an area of space equipped with interactive systems), within the scope of which the visitor interacts by means of his or her eyes, ears, fingers, and by the fact of his or her body moving through the actual area of the exhibition. The intellectual ergonomics of an exhibition provides one of the determining factors capable of developing its didactic character and making it something truly attractive, something which prompts questions and encourages research and discovery. Successful intellectual ergonomics helps visitors to optimise the personal encounter in a system of communications within which they are active and not held prisoner like children sitting on a school bench.

The ergonomic approach to an interactive multimedia exhibition must rest on a certain number of fundamental points. It is appropriate first to recognise and take into account the basic constraints imposed on a visitor to an exhibition. These constraints are four in number: time, energy, money, and information. The first three are rare resources on which we need to economise, while the abundance of the last can lead to a saturation effect, preventing the visitor from deriving any pleasure or motivation. An exhibition which has successful intellectual ergonomics assists the visitor to optimise these four factors, as well as to optimise the effectiveness of the encounter throughout its duration. Accordingly, to achieve this it is important to establish a clear hierarchy among the messages received, in order to facilitate guidance and reduce aimless wandering or queueing – sometimes the only factors spoiling the interest of an exhibition. Studies of the behaviour of visitors when confronted with an unknown stretch of space which they are obliged to conquer intellectually has enabled two different yet widespread attitudes to be distinguished: 'scanning' with the eyes, a visual sweeping of the spaces, panels, themes or sub-themes, which does not involve much energy but which does enable a substantial volume of information to be gathered; and 'zapping' of the feet, moving at random in search of interesting information, a natural response by the visitor confronted with an area of space poor in information content, incomprehensible, or overburdened with details which have been badly arranged and ordered.

In order to avoid passivity, frustration, or saturation with information, the intellectual ergonomics of an exhibition must be supported by a global language, a 'macro language', which is immediately visible and accessible. This should be manifested first in the notices and plans provided before the visit takes place. It should then be followed up in the scenography which creates the distinction between the major objects. Finally, it should appear in the details of the exhibition which lead the visitor from the general to the specific by offering several levels and degrees of abstraction or precision. A guiding thread would then become clearly apparent, an overall message would be conveyed which would form the systemic frame of reference in the course of the detailed and analytic acquisition of the elements of the exhibition. When deprived of intellectual ergonomics, an exhibition can be compared to those modern electronic machines, video recorders, micro-computers, stereo stacks, or film projectors with over complicated operating instructions, control panels overburdened with buttons and switches, and 80 per cent of whose functions are generally useless. Seeing users turn away from these machines which are too difficult to work, designers are now rivalling each other in their ingenuity in redesigning and simplifying controls and instructions, and are re-inventing a kind of tailored ergonomics. The same must apply to a modern exhibition. An exhibition is a communications macro machine, made up of many levels of information transfer, buttons, notices, screens, panels, and animated models. And that is why its user-friendliness, just like the software and hardware of a computer, must be seriously thought out and tested before being put into use.

A multimedia exhibition with good intellectual ergonomics allows for a balance to be met between depth and form, between the scientific and technical content of the messages and the manner in which they are presented. It should also allow for that conflict to be avoided which at present divides the presenters of scientific and technical exhibitions: do we need to give preference to overall understanding or to analysis in detail? The macro approach or micro comprehension? How to present, at a multimedia exhibition, and in a way which will be comprehensible to the greatest number of visitors, themes as complex as biology, ecology, the city, communications, services,

finance, or risk? We need to talk in terms of systems, networks, regulations, flux, evolution; but at the same time, we need to specify details, stimulate reasoning, and provide inspiration for action to be taken. The golden rule from radio and television, 'one idea at a time', applies equally to the elements of an exhibition. But what we need is to know how to insert the details into a broader context which will allow a personalised 'cognitive ecology' to be constructed by way of a dialogue with that global system of communications which is the exhibition. This 'ecology' is a system of interdependent knowledge. This dialectic form of knowledge acquisition causes the knowledge to oscillate permanently from the micro to the macro, from the local to the global, from the analytical to the systemic. What texture should be given to an exhibition in order to favour this dialogue, this constructive dialectical interaction? To achieve this, I propose the creation of an interlaced network of a density which varies depending on the complexity of the messages and which makes recourse to the new concepts of hypertext and fractal images.

Hypertext is a network of interconnected information, within the confines of which it is possible to move, thanks to the guidelines provided by a computer, in step with progress along a multidimensional graph. A button is clicked, and a kind of illustrated compartment materialises at a point on the screen; this leads on to other connections, other sections, texts, graphics, or sounds. Nevertheless, in the course of this interactive guided tour on computer, the totality of the graph is not perceived. A modern interactive exhibition, on the other hand, should be organised like a hypertext of which one would be aware, due to the plan provided with the explanatory notes and the scenography, of the whole of the territory which is to be conquered intellectually. This should apply, moreover, whatever the particular point of interaction with the hypertext network may be, or whatever point may have been reached in the encounter. Each link in the network, as in the case of a hologram, or, better, in a fractal image, must contain the representation of the whole, even if it itself is detailing a particular aspect. A fractal image is a geometric form which remains unchanged whatever the degree of enlargement under which it is being observed. Each micro image contains the macro structure. Likewise, an exhibition of which the intellectual ergonomics of each museographic element is conceived by reference to a fractal approach will recreate at every point the sense of coherence with the entirety of the territory of awareness and knowledge.

The fractal and hypertextual nature of an interactive exhibition will become more and more of a determinant factor in its success and user-friendliness. It will thus also be possible to obtain the balance which is sought between the manner of museographic presentation and the richness of content of the scientific and technical messages being conveyed to the public at large.

Exhibitions and the public understanding of science

Roger Miles and Alan Tout

Is there a distinctive understanding of science that can be conveyed through exhibitions? As we shall show, the existing, soundly based empirical knowledge is insufficient to answer such an ambitious question, though as usual in the museum world opinions and assertions abound. The best we can do is to consider the strengths and weaknesses of exhibitions in educational terms, and use existing research as the basis for a discussion of the potential of exhibitions to affect the public understanding of science.

As the above implies, we believe that to ask what an exhibition conveys to its visitors is an empirical question, best answered by empirical research. There is now a large, and rapidly growing, body of research carried out in museums, science centres, zoos, aquaria and botanic gardens on all aspects of visitors and visitor behaviour. This research has, admittedly, its imperfections. Sample sizes tend to be small, and methodology and statistical analyses often leave much to be desired.[1] Moreover, experimental work in all the social sciences is notoriously difficult to carry out in the field, so its results should always be applied with caution. Nevertheless, there is now a solid tradition of descriptive research going back to Robinson and Melton.[2] This provides tentative rather than well-tested hypotheses about museum visitors and their behaviour, but it is nevertheless an invaluable resource for thinking about, and acting on, museum issues.

Although Robinson and Melton's research was mostly carried out in art galleries (cf [3]), where the apparent simplicity of the exhibits was felt to be an advantage, we shall draw mainly on results obtained in science (including natural history) museums and science centres. The results, incidentally, do not discriminate between museums and science centres as two different types of institution.

'Understanding' is a word sometimes used in connection with visitor studies, and some researchers have employed questions that have at least the potential to reveal any gains in understanding which result from a museum visit.[4] However, most visitor research is overtly concerned with learning. Understanding and learning are different concepts, and it is important at this point to make the difference clear.

For us, learning is the addition of knowledge – of things, including abstract ideas, and of processes – to the memory. Understanding, on the other hand, is akin to what Bruner calls 'grasping the structure of a subject ... in a way that permits many other things to be related to it meaningfully', or learning 'not a skill but a general idea, which can then be used as a basis for recognising subsequent problems as special cases of the idea originally mastered'.[5] Thus it is possible to know something (for example by rote learning) but not understand it, though not the reverse, as discussed elsewhere.[6] The point is worth pressing because it is sometimes suggested that the use of real objects in exhibitions makes possible a unique understanding. There is no apparent evidence to support this proposition, but it suggests an early look at objects and their role in exhibitions.

Traditional museum exhibits show the form, size and colour of the objects they display. They also provide 'physical convincers' that such objects exist, though as Lewis remarks, this important original role of museums (and zoos, aquaria and botanic gardens) has largely been replaced by television and high quality colour printing.[7] Emphatically, objects do not speak for themselves – they are mute on their significance in nature or society – and as far as lay visitors are concerned, the non-verbal language of real things is no more than museological conceit. Of course most displays of objects are accompanied by basic information given in the labels, and visitors are mostly interested in concrete information about the objects on display.[8] This does not alter the fact that isolated snippets of information tend soon to be forgotten, or distorted by tricks of memory.

However the strongest argument against traditional object-and-label exhibits, in the context of the public understanding of science, is that 'the failure to convey relevant concepts will prevent [the visitor] from achieving anything more than an illusion of understanding'.[9] So it seems safe to suggest that objects in exhibitions do not, by simply being there, make possible a distinctive (or indeed any) understanding of science. As a postscript to this argument, it is worth pointing out that much of modern science focuses on the significance of things in nature rather than on the physical evidence of their existence.

We now turn to the empirical evidence of learning in modern multimedia exhibitions which attempt to display both objects and phenomena in an informative context. The research results are mixed. In three major studies, Shettel *et al*[10] and Screven[11] found very little evidence of factual learning among casual visitors, while Borun[12] found a good deal of evidence, particularly among 10- to 14-year olds, and also found evidence of the learning of concepts. Other studies have failed to clarify the situation, but the consensus seems to be that there is very little evidence of learning among casual visitors to exhibitions. This is an unwelcome conclusion, and it has led some to argue that other types of learning must nevertheless be present, such as knowledge of the existence of certain sorts of exhibits, the 'feel' of the architecture, 'that museums are fun places for families to learn in together', 'that parents like to learn, too', and so on.[13] We assume that most students of the public understanding of science would not count this as significant learning.

There is, however, a wider claim to be made for exhibitions as promoters of public understanding. If properly designed, they can serve to awaken interest in science. In addition, because museums are generally non-threatening, convivial institutions, things which are not immediately understood can be enjoyable challenges motivating further exploration, rather than a 'put down' or a 'put off' as is often the case in formal education. Lacking the necessary empirical studies, the first part of this claim is mostly supported by the anecdotal evidence of scientists who were launched on their careers by early visits to museums. Evidence relating to the general public is needed. By 'properly designed' exhibitions we are thinking of something that goes beyond the typical 'ooh, aah' spectacular that fails to teach anything worthwhile.[14]

Visitors and the average visit

Any consideration of the role of exhibitions in the public understanding of science requires a grasp of the relationship between visitor and exhibit. Much research has been carried out in this area.

The first point to make is that the public for museums is limited. On a global scale museums are concentrated in developed countries, and even here their audiences are small in comparison with those for newspapers, radio and television.[15] Hundreds of surveys across the western world have shown that visitors tend to be better educated and from higher socio-economic groups than non-visitors and that technology-based museums attract a disproportionate number of males to females (the Science Museum, London, is a case in point).[16] So there is no question of the public for science in museums being representative of the population as a whole. Some museums have, of course, attempted to broaden their audience by developing exhibitions and events to attract people who would normally not visit them, but so far with limited success.

A visit is typically a social occasion taking place in leisure time, an opportunity to be with family and friends. Visitors are not, with rare exceptions, driven autodidacts, and, with the exception of student parties, they are in a free-choice environment where they set their own agendas. Visitors choose what to see, if anything, and for how long: museum shops, restaurants and toilets, as well as family jokes, group management problems and so on, compete with the exhibits for the visitors' attention. Apparently one-third of visitors to major museums in the western world do not even enter the exhibition galleries.[17]

Few visits to museums last much more than two hours of which perhaps half is devoted to the exhibits; and because most visitors are making their first visit, they attempt to see everything, to 'do' the whole museum. Research from a wide variety of sources suggests that an average visit has the following characteristics:

i The visitor is moving most of the time, exploring the museum to get the feel of whole exhibitions rather than individual exhibits.[18]

ii Most exhibits are inspected casually with only a few, which may differ from visitor to visitor, engaging the attention for any length of time. Stops at exhibits range from 0 to 45 minutes, but generally they average less than 30 seconds.[19]

iii Most attention is paid to exhibits during the first 30 minutes of the visit; subsequently visitors stop less and stay for less time, and the number of exhibits stopped at for a long time diminishes progressively during the visit.[20]

It is desirable, of course, to look beyond these studies of gross visitor behaviour to gain some idea of how visitors feel and think about exhibitions. Alt, Shaw, and Griggs have studied how visitors perceive exhibits.[21] Alt and Shaw asked visitors not only how well the exhibits worked for them, but also how they rated them against their conception of an ideal exhibit. Using this technique they were able to draw up a spectrum from positive attributes which ideal exhibits should have, through neutral to negative attributes which would be absent in an ideal (see table 1). Griggs extended this approach to investigate which attributes visitors used to discriminate between traditional and modern exhibitions. Among other outcomes, this enabled him to draw up lists of desirable and undesirable exhibition characteristics (see table 2).

The phenomenon of museum fatigue was intently studied in the early days of research into the behaviour of visitors,[22] with the conclusion that it is caused by psychological rather than physical factors, or in Lewis' words, by 'saturating students with more information than they can handle'.[23]

These studies are worthy of attention because even now few exhibitions are designed to lessen the problem of information overload and to pace the visit, and all too often exhibition designs run counter to the positive and desirable characteristics identified in tables 1 and 2.

The potential

We have alluded above to the communicative incompetence displayed by many exhibitions; we have also noted how visitors behave in museums and how they perceive the exhibits in relation to their more general expectations. Exhibitions, however, also have potential strengths in relation to the understanding of science. These strengths are concerned with the variety of communications media, messages and visitor characteristics, and their potentially fruitful interaction.

Museums may well be unique in that they are able, in principle, to use all the media of communication (although they may be constrained in their choice by financial and practical considerations). The range of media is tentatively summarised in tables 3 and 4, to which, in the absence of a stable terminology, the following notes should be added:

i Museums are not restricted to communicating via exhibits. The available media may be incorporated in exhibits (table 3), or used in other modes detached from the exhibits (table 4).

ii Exhibit media are either static or dynamic (they do or do not undergo a change of state).

iii Dynamic media are used in the automaton mode (running automatically), operand mode (giving a simple, fixed response to the visitor's command), or interactive mode (in which exhibit and visitor react to the actions of each other in a way not fully determined).

iv Operand and interactive exhibits are the extremes of a continuum of hands-on or participatory types.

v Exhibit media are normally used in combinations ranging from the traditional object-plus-typescript exhibit to immersion experiences, which may employ six or more media to recreate the experience of a particular time and place.[24]

vi Detached media (table 4) may be employed as adjuncts to the exhibits (sharing the same subject matter), or they may stand alone as independent pieces of communication.

The variety present in the available media can be used to counter museum fatigue caused by the monotonous presentation of information.

The second potential advantage of this variety is that media can be chosen to match the messages to be communicated. Common sense suggests some simple rules in selecting media, so that dynamic events require dynamic exhibits, but so far research has not provided strong guidelines in this area. Selecting media (and combining them in paced sequences) remains one of the big challenges of exhibition design: the act of selection remains an art rather than a science. Some research has, however, been carried out on the effectiveness of media in exhibitions: Peart[25] and Bitgood et al[26] have confirmed the primacy of typescript in communicating information, and a long series of authors from Melton onwards have demonstrated the superiority of participatory exhibits in attracting and holding the attention of visitors.

The third potential advantage of variety, in the media of communication, is the opportunity this affords the designer to match the exhibits to different learning styles and modalities among visitors. Although museums have long been aware of variety in the demographics of their audiences, it is only recently that attention has focused on differences in psychology and behaviour.

'Learning style' refers to the fact that people learn

in different ways, and 'modalities' to the preferred senses through which they receive information.[27] Thus exhibitions are able to accommodate visitors who like to read (linguistic intelligence), look at audio-visuals (spatial intelligence), be actively involved with exhibits (bodily-kinesthetic intelligence), solve problems (logical-mathematical intelligence) and so on. So far little research has been carried out in exhibitions on these topics, but one interesting result to come out of McManus' work is how learning-related behaviour varies with the grouping of the visitors.[28] Solitary visitors are likely to read but very unlikely to participate in hands-on exhibits; couples are likely to read but unlikely to participate; groups composed only of adults are unlikely to read and likely to participate only if females are present; and groups of adults and children are unlikely to read but very likely to participate. It seems an obvious conclusion that exhibitions should employ a wide range of media, and that there should be considerable redundancy of information spread across the different types.

Conclusions

Exhibitions undoubtedly enjoy other advantages over the formal educational system that we have not mentioned.[29] We have concentrated here on what appear to be their particular advantages in comparison with mass media such as television, radio and magazines. That said, it seems that these advantages are not recognised in most museums, so that the museum's potential to play a significant

role in the public understanding of science is more impressive than the performance. A major concern is that the tasks of planning, designing, and criticising science exhibitions are mostly carried out in ignorance of the scientific research most relevant to these tasks (physician, heal thyself!).

Given the almost universal acceptance of the need for communicators to know their audience and speak to it in a language tailor-made to its requirements, there is still a worrying gap, in most museum exhibitions, between the people they are designed for and the people who come. Science can only be communicated successfully if a sensible relationship is struck between the target and actual audiences; in other words, if what is to be said and how, are tempered with knowledge of and respect for the visitors. Scientists must, in short, design not for themselves and their peers, but for the public as it really is, and as it really uses museums. The prejudice, tradition and assertion typically deployed in designing exhibitions must yield to knowledge, or museums will remain a scientists' private game. Experience at the Natural History Museum suggests that one balances the chance of succeeding in making science understandable to the visiting public against the risk of failing in the eyes of critics. But museums are there for the benefit of visitors.

Acknowledgements

We are grateful to Dr Giles Clarke for commenting on our first draft.

Table 1. *Relationship of exhibit characteristics to the ideal. Taken from research carried out in the Natural History Museum, London.*

Negative	Neutral	Positive
Badly placed	Participatory	Makes the subject come to life
Lacking in information	Better than textbooks	Makes point quickly
Visitors distracted by other displays	Artistic	Suitable for all ages
Confusing	Makes a difficult subject easier	Memorable

Table 2. Desirable and undesirable characteristics of exhibitions listed in descending order of importance. Taken from research carried out in the Natural History Museum, London.

Undesirable characteristics	Desirable characteristics
Subject matter not sufficiently explained	Clear to visitor where to begin and how to continue
Exhibits not realistic enough: difficult to relate to the real world	Uses modern display techniques to help visitor learn
Appealing to children rather than adults	Uses familiar objects and experiences
Traditional, old fashioned	Comprehensive display of objects

Table 3. Some of the main media of communication in exhibits: classification by mode of action.

Static media	Dynamic media		
	Automaton mode	Operand mode	Interactive mode
Models	Models	Mechanical devices	
Mounted animals			
Dioramas			
Replicas			
Illustrations	Audio-visuals	Audio-visuals	
Diagrams	Graphics embodying movement	Graphics embodying movement	
Typescript	Dot-matrix displays	Flip panels	Computer-based exhibits with or without video disk

Table 4. Some of the main detached media of communication: classification by mode of use.

	Stand alone	Exhibit adjuncts
Face to face	Lectures	Lectures
	Demonstrations	Demonstrations
	Theatre	Theatre
		Guided tours
Distance teaching	Books	Audio taped guides
	Films	Printed guides
	Radio and TV	Catalogues
	Videos	Films
	Computers	Radio and TV
		Videos
		Computers

Notes and references

1 Miles, R S, and Tout, A F, 'The impact of research on the approach to the visiting public at the Natural History Museum, London', *International Journal of Science Education*, 13 (in press 1991)
Koran, J J Jr, and Ellis, J, 'Research in informal settings: some reflections on designs and methodology', *ILVS Review*, 2, 1 (1991), pp67-86

2 Robinson, E S, *The Behavior of the Museum Visitor* (Washington, DC: American Association of Museums, 1928)
Melton, A W, *Problems of Installation in Museums of Art* (Washington, DC: American Association of Museums, 1935)

3 Melton, A W, 'Distribution of attention in galleries in a museum of science and industry', *Museum News*, 14, 3 (1936), pp6-8

4 Blud, L M, 'Social interaction and learning among family groups visiting a museum', *Museum Management and Curatorship*, 9 (1991), pp43-51

5 Bruner, J S, *The Process of Education* (Cambridge, MA: Harvard University Press, 1978)

6 Miles, R S, *et al*, *The Design of Educational Exhibits* (London: Unwin Hyman, 2nd ed, 1988)

7 Lewis, B N, 'The museum as an educational facility', *Museums Journal*, 80, 3 (1980), pp151- 5

8 Kropf, M B, 'The family museum experience: a review of the literature', *Journal of Museum Education*, 14, 2 (1989), pp5-8

9 Lewis, B N

10 Shettel, H, *et al*, *Strategies for Determining Exhibit Effectiveness* (Pittsburgh, PA: American Institutes for Research, 1968)

11 Screven, C G, *The Measurement and Facilitation of Learning in the Museum Environment: An Experimental Analysis* (Washington, DC: Smithsonian Press, 1974)

12 Borun, M, *Measuring the Immeasurable: A Pilot Study of Museum Effectiveness* (Washington, DC: Association of Science-Technology Centers, 1977)

13 Dierking, L D, 'The family museum experience: implications from research', *Journal of Museum Education*, 14, 2 (1989), pp9-11

14 Lewis, B N

15 Miles, R S, 'Museums and the communication of science', in Evered, D and O'Connor, M (eds), *Communicating Science to the Public* (London: John Wiley & Sons, 1987)

16 Hood, M G, 'Staying away: why people choose not to visit museums', *Museum News*, 61, 4 (1983), pp50-7
Merriman, N, 'Museum visiting as a cultural phenomenon' in Vergo, P (ed), *The New Museology* (London: Reaktion Books, 1989)
Kelly, R F, 'Museums as status symbols III: a speculative examination of motives among those who love being in museums, those who go to have been, and those who refuse to go' (paper presented at the Visitor Studies Conference, Ottawa, August 1991)
Borun, M, and Miller, M, 'To label or not to label?', *Museum News*, 58, 4 (1980), pp64-7

17 Kelly, R F

18 Kropf, M B
Borun, M, and Miller, M
Diamond, J, 'The behavior of family groups in science museums', *Curator*, 29, 2 (1986), pp139-54

19 Beer, V, 'Great expectations: do museums know what visitors are doing?', *Curator*, 30, 3 (1987), pp206-15

20 Melton, A W (1935)
Dierking, L
Diamond, J
Lakota, R A, *The National Museum of Natural History as a Behavioral Environment* (Washington, DC: Smithsonian Office of Museum Programs, 1976)
Falk, J H, *et al*, 'Predicting visitor behaviour', *Curator*, 28, 4 (1985), pp249-57

21 Alt, M B and Shaw, K M, 'Characteristics of ideal museum exhibits', *British Journal of Psychology*, 75 (1984), pp25-36
Griggs, S A, 'Perceptions of traditional and new style exhibitions at the Natural History Museum, London', *ILVS Review*, 1, 2 (1990), pp78-90

22 Robinson, E S
Melton, A W (1935)

23 Lewis, B N

24 Bitgood, S, *The Role of Simulated Immersion in Exhibitions* (Jacksonville, AL: Center for Social Design, Technical Report No. 90-20, 1990)

25 Peart, B, 'Impact of exhibit type on knowledge gain, attitude, and behavior', *Curator*, 27, 3 (1984), pp220-37

26 Bitgood, S, *et al*, *Effects of Label Characteristics*

on Visitor Behavior (Jacksonville, AL: Center for Social Design, Technical Report No. 86-55, 1986)

27 Serrell, B, 'Learning styles and museum visitors', in Serrell, B (ed), *What Research Says About Learning in Science Museums* (Washington, DC: Association of Science-Technology Centers, 1990)
Dierking, L D, 'Learning theory and learning styles: an overview', *Journal of Museum Education*, 16, 1 (1991), pp4-6

Gilbert, E R, 'Using the learning style inventory', *Journal of Museum Education*, 16, 1 (1991), pp7-9

28 McManus, P M, 'It's the company you keep ... the social determination of learning-related behavior in a science museum', *Museum Management and Curatorship*, 6 (1987), pp263-70

29 Bitgood, S, *A Comparison of Formal and Informal Learning* (Jacksonville, AL: Center for Social Design, Technical Report No. 88-10, 1988).

The medium is the museum: on objects and logics in times and spaces

Roger Silverstone

I would like to offer some thoughts on the particular character of the museum as a medium of communication, and to provide a framework for its analysis. In doing so I will draw on recently completed research, based at the Science Museum, London, which examined the processes through which a new gallery in the Museum was created and which undertook visitor research in the light of that examination.[1]

The New Museology recommends that both the study of museums and professional work within museums should adopt a greater degree of self awareness, enquiring not just into methods, but into purpose, context and consequence.[2] The museum is no longer, if ever it was, an institution innocently engaged in the processes of the collection, conservation, classification, and display of objects. On the contrary, it is one among many components in a complex array of cultural and leisure industries,[3] no longer certain of its role, no longer secure in its identity, no longer isolated from political and economic pressures or from the explosion of images and meanings which are, arguably, transforming our relationships in contemporary society to time, space and reality.[4]

One possible route towards self awareness is a consideration of the museum as medium. Such a proposition, of course, implies both that there is something distinctive about the museum's mediation of the world, and that that distinctiveness has particular consequences for our understanding of the museum's significance. So what kind of medium is the museum? How do museums relate to, and participate in, the wider mediated culture of the late twentieth century? What can we learn about museums by drawing on that body of research and writing that has taken the study of contemporary media, most significantly television, as its focus? Museums are in many respects like other contemporary media. They entertain and inform; they tell stories and construct arguments; they aim to please and to educate; they define, consciously or unconsciously, effectively or ineffectively, an agenda; they translate the otherwise unfamiliar and inaccessible into the familiar and accessible. And in the construction of their texts, their displays, their technologies, they offer an ideologically inflected account of the world.

But equally, of course, there are obvious differences between museums and other media such as newspapers, radio or television. Museums occupy physical space; they contain objects; they encourage interactivity; they allow the visitor, literally, to wander through their texts; and even temporary exhibitions have a permanence uncharacteristic of other media.

As media, museums increasingly have to compete with other media for attention and for visitors; they come to depend on other media, particularly video and interactive computer-based technologies, within their own exhibitions; and they have to rely on other media both as sources of information and as mediators of their own products as their own exhibitions are marketed and reviewed in the same way as other cultural events are.

I have subtitled this paper, 'objects and logics in times and spaces'. Increasingly it is being recognised that the distinctive character of modern media lies in their capacity to articulate and to transform relations to time and space. Their mediation results in shifts in society's relationship to time and space. Television news, for example, always present, brings a sense of instant contact irrespective of both geographical and temporal distance. The televising of national events provides the basis for the invention of new, and the resurrection of old, communities.[5] In addition, studies of the media have focused on the particular logics of texts: the narrative structures of programmes, the rhetoric of discourses, the structures of argument, and of course the role of the viewer/reader in constructing or reconstructing all of these. Also studies of the media look at the ways in which verisimilitude is created: a sense of realism without which no trust in the medium could be sustained.

In focusing on the museum, therefore, it is these neo-Kantian categories – logic, time, and space – that will provide the framework, though the starting point is of a different order. Perhaps the single most obvious, and most determining, characteristic of the museum is the necesssary presence within it of objects, things which by their presence in the museum, claim a particular status – unique, significant, representative.

The object

Objects have biographies. They move through a world of public and private arenas, and in and out of the world of goods and commodities, born in a factory, an artist's studio or a craftsman's workshop, they may end up on a scrap heap, on a mantlepiece, or in the glass case of a museum. As Igor Kopytoff suggests, material objects, like people, have not one biography but many. For example a car will have an economic biography, 'its initial worth, its sale and resale price, the rate of decline in its value, its response to the recession, the patterning over several years of its maintenance costs', but it will also have several social biographies:

> one biography may concentrate on its place in the owner-family's economy, another may relate the history of its ownership to the society's class structure, and a third may focus on its role in the sociology of the family's kin relations, such as loosening family ties in America or strengthening them in Africa.[6]

The point of course is that the biography of an object gains its meaning through the various social, economic, political, and cultural environments through which it passes, and its passage can in turn illuminate those environments in the way that a flare or a tracer can illuminate the night sky.

As Charles Saumarez-Smith suggests, neither the biography of an object nor the museum's own contribution to that biography are straightforward.[7] It is a commonplace to observe that objects in museums are more often than not divorced from the world which bore them and in which they gained their various meanings. It is also a commonplace to observe that objects in museums are fixed in their meaning, now that they have reached their final resting place and been included in a collection and placed (or not) on display. However there is, as Saumarez-Smith argues, life after death, even in a museum – or at least a life of a sort. A sculpture of a Saxon god still pockmarked and lichened from its life in various English country gardens, a late seventeenth-century doorway and a late seventeenth-century interior, all have been transformed by their passage through the Victoria and Albert Museum: the statue is uncomfortably displayed alongside elegantly restored and polished sculptures of different origin and aesthetic intention; the door has become a shop fitting and a company logo; and the room is wrapped in polythene awaiting a decision on its ultimate fate.

In the gallery which was the focus of our research, *Food for Thought: the Sainsbury Gallery*, a permanent exhibition which opened in the Science Museum, London, in October 1989, some of the objects displayed are entirely familiar to the visitor, but at the same time the shock of the unfamiliarity of their display in the museum requires the visitor to rethink. A McDonalds interior, a supermarket check-out, offer a firm link between the everyday world of the consumer/visitor and the exhibition in the museum. Other objects, less familiar perhaps, including various food production technologies, make other claims. They offer an account of the production process that says little of those who operated the machines or the conditions under which they worked. Similarly, and perhaps more conventionally, the exhibition includes 'historical' objects – models of kitchen interiors with original artefacts, examples of early packaging – each with their own biographies, each 'rescued' by their inclusion in the gallery and their mute appeals to the visitor to complete their meaning.

The museum's work in constructing particular biographies for its objects as justification for their inclusion in the collection or display results in an abstraction. The ensuing meanings are of necessity partial, but more importantly they are an essential part of the particular claims for authority and legitimacy on which the museum's whole status depends. It is, after all, through the object, and through the object's membership of a collection, that the distinct character of the museum is achieved.

Two things complicate matters even further, particularly in the contemporary exhibition. The first complication lies in the recognition that the meaning of an object does not stop with its display, nor is it determined either by its place in the display or the description offered of it in the adjoining label. The meaning of an object continues in the imaginative work of the visitor who brings to it his or her own agenda, experiences and feelings. As Ludmilla Jordanova points out, the object in the museum becomes a kind of fetish, an object of exaggerated attention, frozen in time and space, an expression of the claims of mastery that are inscribed within the very fabric of the museum.[8] It has a magic potency. The object invites a kind of identification with the Other, at once distanced and close at hand. This dialectic of distance and accessibility, of course, is a commonplace in accounts of the workings of the contemporary media. Indeed, it is possible to see it as a central defining characteristic of them: the familiar made strange; the strange made familiar. Yet both the attention and identification claimed rhetorically by the display of objects cannot be guaranteed merely by their display and classification. Visitors are actively engaged in what they see.

The second complication, and one dramatically revealed in the *Food for Thought* gallery, is provided by the inclusion in the exhibition of non-objects – mock-ups, audio-visual technologies, interactive computer information points, panels of text and illustrations – which provide another, but quite different, claim to be providing an experience of the real. Alan Morton argues that the increasing trend to appropriate new technologies and media by the museum and to include examples of them as part of a multimedia interactive experience, has turned museums into commodities.[9] The commodification of the museum echoes and reinforces the commodification of the objects that the museum displays. The reality that is being claimed through these media objects, is a reality grounded in the experience of everyday life, and of the domination of the mass media in that experience. So alongside the claims of objects grounded in the authority of the past and in the authority of the curator, these technologies make their claims through the familiarity, security and seductions of what Umberto Eco and Jean Baudrillard would see as the 'hyper-real' – the over-mediated world of simulation and self-referentiality which we seem in our daily lives to take entirely for granted.[10]

One final point concerning the status of the object in the museum is eloquently made by Eugene Donato:

> The set of objects the Museum displays is sustained only by the fiction that they somehow constitute a coherent representational universe ... Should the fiction disappear, there is nothing left of the *Museum* but "bric-a-brac", a heap of meaningless and valueless fragments of objects which are incapable of substituting themselves either metonymically for the original objects or metaphorically for their representations.[11]

An object is nothing unless it is part of a collection. A collection is nothing unless it can successfully lay claim to a logic of classification which removes it from the arbitrary or the occasional.[12] In its work of collection the museum provides both a model for, and an echo of, the work of consumption in which we all engage, extracting from a world of commercial values objects which gain their meaning by their inclusion in our own symbolic universe.[13]

However there is clearly more to the museum than the work of classification, and while objects may well gain their authority from their place in a classificatory system, they also gain their meaning from their place in a display. Once again, as I have argued elsewhere, the meaning of an object or of an exhibition is significantly dependent on the 'curatorial' work of the visitor in which objects are re-inscribed into a personal culture of memory and experience.[14] But even the possibility of this reconstruction is based on the existence of a display which may or may not be ordered by the logic which informed the collection.

It is to the question of logic – the logics of display – that I now turn.

Logics

Museums are communicating environments in which complex meanings are negotiated. Those meanings are only partly dependent on the meanings ascribed to individual objects by their place in an historical, an archaeological, or an aesthetic classificatory system. As Tony Bennett suggests in his comparison of three different museums, objects which on the face of it seem remarkably similar are displayed in very different ways in each with potentially significant ideological consequences.[15]

Donna Harraway describes the representational activities of museums as the deployment of 'technologies of enforced meaning'.[16] At the heart of these activities is an attempt to create a realist text, in which the aim is a kind of transparency: this is how it was; this is how it is; this is how it will be. What is at issue, as Harraway demonstrates, is the particular character and claim of the museum as a textual phenomenon, and the relative degree of openness and closure that it desires or appears to offer the visitor/reader.

Museums, galleries, and exhibitions are texts constructed according to a variety of logics. They have emerged as a result of a complex interplay of institutional and individual forces[17] and are consumed in a multitude of different ways by visitors. But they appear as anything but arbitrary. They are structured according to their own rhetoric, a rhetoric which seeks to persuade the visitor that what is being seen and read is important, beautiful, true. They are also structured narratively, by principles of classification and representation which create stories, arguments, or sometimes more open logics, and which provide frameworks or routes through which the visitors pass and which help them make sense of what they have seen.

It is, of course, the case that individual galleries or exhibitions, never mind museums as wholes, may express multiple logics. A sense of these logics is given form by the existence of galleries built at different times within the same museum, or the existence of different museums within an identifiable genre of collection and representation. A classificatory logic may overlap a historical sequence, a scheme often seen in classical museums of science and technology where the grand narrative of progress is inscribed in the arrangements of, and reflections in, the ubiquitous glass cases. A historical narrative may be grounded in a number of different and overlapping histories, as it is for example in the Museum of the Moving Image in London, where histories of the technologies of moving images (from the camera obscura to the cartoon and the computer) co-exist with a more dominant history of their products and production processes. As it happens MOMI is a particularly significant example of a closed narrative structure. The constraints imposed by the site (but not only those constraints) appear to have encouraged the creators of the museum to impose a relatively inflexible linear structure on the exhibition. A single route is marked intermittently by labels indicating how much has been seen and how much is still to go.

Narratives, historical or otherwise, do provide a framework for the display of objects in the museum. The stories that are told about them and the larger stories in which they are the actors provide a particular form of closure that may or may not be followed or recreated by the visitor. Visitors literally walk, or are propelled, through the stories which museums provide for them in their

displays. But in so doing, within the limits of the varying degrees of freedom they are given, they create their own versions of the narratives on offer.[18]

Somewhere embedded in these narratives, is, as Robert Bud argues, a version of myth:

> a specially authentic, intense, or direct contact with the sacred subject, be it historical event or current development, in a sphere with the power, danger and distance of science ... the museum acts to reduce fear and provide 'understanding' of the special phenomenon ... the museum as a religious centre is an established phenomenon.[19]

Bud's account of the making of the Chemical Industry gallery at the Science Museum in London is, of course, another museological narrative. It tells of the inevitable compromises in gallery design under pressure of what he calls 'the machine': the machine of organisational, political, and economic forces; the machine of the often arbitrary and haphazard processes of gallery production.

Yet what emerges, compromised or not, is presented as neither arbitrary nor haphazard. Something of the quality of myth remains, structured into the stories of the achievements of science and technology and in the containing metaphors and metonymies of the display of the objects themselves.[20] What emerges, too, of course, is a particular inflection of that myth, of necessity ideological, and in one way or another expressing a world view which excludes or relegates into insignificance other versions of reality.

The *Food for Thought* gallery did not emerge fully formed. The story of its creation and of the emergence of its dominating logic is one that will easily be recognised by those who have experience of such work.[21] Early decisions, for example, not to tell a single story about food – either grounded historically or in terms of a narrative of production and consumption – were sustained. But the preferred logic of themes and topics took some time to become fixed, and the final structure of a pyramidal logic in which wider messages subsumed smaller ones had a number of consequences for the later inclusion of specific ideas and materials.[22] In particular this had consequences for the representation of controversy. Such a logic, in its relative openness, also had consequences for the visitor.

The decision to present the science and technology of food and nutrition in this relatively open way was informed by a desire to create a gallery committed to the public understanding of science and as a result to grounding the science of food and nutrition in the experience of the everyday. As it happens the gallery also had a number of different points of physical, and therefore logical, entry, so a single narrative would have been difficult to impose. Visitors were therefore presented with an open structure whose logic was perhaps clear to the curators but not fully declared. In the event, visitors' retrospective accounts of the visit provided little evidence of their capacity either to reproduce 'the logic' of the exhibition or indeed to produce a narrative of their own, except perhaps in a fragmented version. Their accounts of the gallery, informed by their own progress through it but also by prior expectations and experiences, were often disjointed and presented in ways which suggested that they recognised that they had not 'done the gallery properly'. Buried in these fragmented accounts of their visit, however, was a sense of the gallery as providing either a history of food and nutrition or a structured exercise in health education.[23]

Central to an understanding of the museum as medium, therefore, are the logics which underpin the arrangement of the objects on display. Such logics are not determined by the principles by which the objects in the collection have been classified (though they might be), and even those principles are not consistent (compare, for example the ethnographic collections of the Pitt-Rivers Museum in Oxford to the Museum of Mankind in London or to Paolozzi's Lost Magic Kingdom.)[24] Histories of discrete areas of science or technology, biographies of artists expressed in the arrangements of their work, pedagogically oriented structures or arguments in favour of one interpretation of material culture over another, all in their various ways can provide, singly or multiply, a framework for the museum's textuality. It can be relatively open or it can aim for closure. In either event the framework is not ideologically neutral, nor is it unconstrained or inconsequential in its effects. Especially significant for the present argument, and especially important for understanding, once again, the particularity of the museum as medium, are the exhibition's relationships to time and space.

Times

Time is itself a medium. I have already referred to

aspects of the museum's relationship to time, in its production, in its articulation of myth, history and memory, and in the work of visitors. The museum, perhaps most supremely in contemporary culture, is seen as an institution for the mediation of time. As often as not, it represents the Other removed in time: the historical Other. But this truism masks much diversity and complexity in the temporality of the museum. I can barely do justice to this complexity here, so once again I will try and focus on those aspects of the museum's temporality that bear centrally on its status as a medium of communication.

There is a strand in media research and criticism which finds in the explosion of electronic communication in the late twentieth century a fundamental challenge to our customary experience of both space and time. The following quotation from Patricia Mellencamp is typical of those discussions of media and technology which see them as having a fundamental affect on the infrastructures of society, culture, and consciousness:

> US network television is a disciplinary time machine, a metronome rigorously apportioning the present, rerunning TV history, and anxiously awaiting the future. The hours, days, and television seasons are seriated, scheduled and traded in ten-second increments modelled on the modern work week – day time, prime time, late night or weekend. Time itself is a gendered, hierarchized commodity capitalizing on leisure.[25]

The museum, though less ubiquitous and therefore less powerful than television, does offer a distinct kind of temporality, and one that is arguably changing both in response to changes in the media environment and by its incorporation of those media technologies into its own displays. But before we run away with the idea that mediation is all powerful, and that the times of the museum (the representation of the past, the immediacy of the present, the extrapolations into the future), are overwhelming in their effects, we must remember that at the very least there are two significant temporalities involved in the experience of the museum: that of the museum itself and that of the visitor.[26]

One way of approaching these difficult issues is to borrow a conceptualisation of the social construction of time developed in some of the literature in family therapy.[27] Here a distinction is made between orienting and clocking. Orienting refers to the selection, direction and maintenance of attitudes and behaviours towards the past, present and future, and to non-temporal realms of experience, by emphasising one or more of these realms or of the particular relationships among them. Museums, like families, it can be argued, define for themselves a dominating orientation to time which provides a framework for the culture of the institution and for the representations of science, art or culture which they contain. Orientation does not refer only to the representational activities of the museum, however. It also refers to its organisational activities: for example, whether the museum as an organisation defines its activities principally in relation to the past (a kind of atavism in which old collections are preserved and displays protected), to the present (a kind of entrepreneurialism in which the museum constantly adjusts its priorities and designs its galleries in response to immediately felt needs and pressures), or to the future (a kind of conservationism in which emphasis is placed on collection and conservation at the expense of display). Orienting can also refer to the particular character of a gallery in which the same kinds of decisions, embodied in the texts of the exhibition, are expressed. In comparison with other Science Museum galleries, *Food for Thought* is significantly oriented to the present grounded in an appeal to the visitor's own daily life. This is of course reinforced by the presence of so much in the way of contemporary media and other technologies.

Clocking refers to 'the regulation of the sequence, frequency, duration and pace of immediately experienced events from moment to moment, hour to hour, and day to day'.[28] Whereas orientation is, in the context of the museum or the gallery, a relatively undynamic, unnegotiable, invisible quality, clocking is dynamic, visible, and open to negotiation.

From the point of view of the curators and designers of a gallery, clocking consists of the efforts to define the dynamics of its internal logic. Narrative, the particular arrangement of exhibits in space, the physical, intellectual or aesthetic links between them, the assessment of concentration span in relation to specific exhibits, the attempts to control a visitor's movement through the gallery, these are all aspects of clocking strategies evident in all museum galleries.

Clocking, in the context of such activities, is a bid for control over the environment created for the display, but more especially for control over the visitor's progress through that environment. And it is here, of course, that the problems arise. Patricia Mellencamp's description of the particular temporality of US television is a description of a deeply engrained rhetorical bid for the medium's articulation of the times of daily life, both orientational and in terms of our clocking schedules. Such bids may be visible in texts, in programme schedules, and in the fragmentation of programmes and their narrative structure, just as such bids may be visible in the structure of a museum's texts. But the museum presents a different kind of temporality, more physical and grounded in a face-to-face present, less compelling in its exclusion of other realities, other forms of mediation. The result is, even at its most extreme, a multiply open text, in which visitors will bring to bear their own orientations (do they match those defined for them in the exhibition?) and clocking (choosing a route through the gallery and according a particular time to the visit as a whole and to individual exhibits). Pace, sequence, duration and scheduling are all aspects of the visitors' clocking mechanism, and their times are not necessarily those anticipated by the designers.

Yet some matching of the orientation and clocking of both exhibition and visitor will have to take place if the communication in which the gallery engages can be considered successful. Indeed the range of meaningful freedoms that the visitor has is inevitably constrained, both as a result of a kind of acclimatisation to the temporality of the museum and a readiness to be directed through the gallery in the terms implicitly or explicitly stated in its design and construction.[29]

Spaces

Time in the museum remains, in all its manifestations, intangible. Less so space. The museum, unique among contemporary media, provides a physical embodiment of space: a geographical, an architectural environment which once again, though for different reasons, masks the complexity of the various spatially related relationships which characterise the museum's mode of communication.

Of course, in a literal sense space provides one of the key constraints on gallery design. The shape of it, the amount of it, its quality and accessibility, all are crucial material factors at every stage of the creation of a new exhibition.[30] The dimensions of a visit, the likely route a visitor will take through a gallery, the need to structure the exhibits so that a variety of different routes can be catered for, are all well-known problems for museum designers.[31] Yet the spatial dimensions of the museum's communication extend well beyond these albeit vital, practical considerations.

I want to consider museum space both materially and phenomenologically primarily with reference to the *Food for Thought* gallery. The gallery occupies space previously devoted to the astronomy collection. It takes up 810m². Within those 810m² are 166 interactives, working demonstrations, videos, computer information points, objects and replica sets. The average number of objects per square metre is 0.1 (compared with 0.6 in the museum as a whole). These individual exhibits are incorporated in a gallery that has been carefully designed and structured in accordance with a logic built around questions and answers, themes and topics. No overall narrative structure was imposed on the gallery. No arrows mark a preferred progress, a preferred reading. Within the gallery, various subsections, though not always clearly identified as such, focus on food consumption and food production, with sub-themes, for example, on diet, additives, and food safety. At many stages of the design and production process planned exhibits were withdrawn because of lack of space.[32]

Space in the museum, then, is a finite resource. It is also a territory, more or less jealously taken over and guarded. And it is also, of course, a phenomenological reality, a set of perceptions subject to constant structuring and restructuring in the imagination and experiences of all those involved in the museum's mediation of the world.

Anthony Giddens writes of the quality of space and time in modern societies in terms of space-time distancing. Electronic media have, he suggests, removed us from the close-knit networks of face-to-face communication and attachment to place which were the norm for those living in pre-modern societies. Watching television, making a telephone call, receiving instantaneous financial information on a global computer network, are activities which have fundamentally affected our relationships to, and our perceptions of, space and time. Space, in particular, has become dematerialised. The museum is both part of this world and not part of it. I have already noted that it increasingly incorporates (and maybe even relies on) those very technologies which Giddens claims have

altered our sense of space, and our own position in space. Yet, quite obviously, at least for the time being, museums remain traditional spatial environments requiring a physical journey and physical movement through an exhibition.

Increasingly, new galleries, especially in science and technology, are becoming media hybrids. They are grafting two kinds of spatial orientation together. The first is one in which objects are both displayed in a structured space and at the same time refer to a space outside the walls of the museum in which they have another, distant, significance. This is how the 'traditional' museum might be described. The objects act as media, metonymically related, in their displacement, to other places. The second kind of spatial orientation is provided by the secondary mediation of those objects through the images and sounds of electronic media on the one hand, and the interactive experience on the other. Videos provide immediacy and realism, often at the expense of the objects themselves. They become metaphors of the real, no longer imagined, but trusted as accurate representations of other places and other times. Interactives have a different, but related, spatial significance, offering the opportunity for the visitor to transcend the otherwise unbridgeable distance between his or her individual space and the world of the Other. Both these media, once incorporated into the museum, blur the boundaries between the museum's private space and the public world, a boundary which was pretty well held when both objects and visitors had to cross the same threshold. But they also blur the boundaries between the individual's private space and the public space of the museum, in this case reinforcing the familiar elision of domestic and public that the consumption of television in particular, tends to produce.[33]

Yet visitors do still have to come to the museum. When they come they are faced with a physical arrangement of objects, images and texts through which they will pass and of which they may make some sense. That space is in a number of senses a *potential* space.[34] It is a space in which visitors are offered, and of necessity accept, an invitation to create and to complete the experience of being in the museum. Visitors are offered a more or less containing and structured environment through which they move and within which they can, in every sense of the word, play in a safe world, an extension of childhood involvement with other objects. They construct their own narratives more or less creatively, more or less securely, in the space physically provided for them in the arrangement of the gallery, and metaphorically provided for them in the extension of that space to include their own experience. This potential space which surrounds and contains any act of communication is an essential part of the museum's communication. The objects that are displayed within it gain their meaning and their power both from their significance as items in a collection and their claims for authenticity, but also from the imaginative work that visitors can and must do in relation to them. Their aura and their magic, the aura and magic of the exhibition or museum as a whole, is a product of the joint creative work undertaken in this potential space.

The consuming visitor

It may seem perverse to lay so much emphasis on the visitor in these discussions of the museum as a medium. And it would be wrong to read into my account a sense of the visitor's exclusive priority. Yet, perhaps more now than ever before, the visitor – the consuming visitor – has become increasingly important not only in any theoretical consideration of the medium, but increasingly also in the process of gallery and exhibition creation itself. Again, perhaps, this has been particularly true in the UK where, since the early 1980s, a market-based ideology has permeated all aspects of society, leaving few areas of public service and cultural provision untouched. Consumers have become the kings and queens of the market-place. In the museum the increasing significance of 'public understanding' especially in relation to

science and technology has provided an insistent framework for gallery design. The visitor is encoded in the texts of the museum in a way that can scarcely have been the case in earlier years.

Maybe the current preoccupation, in the literature, with the receivers of mass media is part of the same ideological shift. It is self evidently the case that any understanding of the process and dynamics of the media in contemporary society cannot exclude a concern with reception. The status of the object in the museum; the plausibility, persuasiveness and the offered pleasures of the museum's texts; the representation and articulation of space and time, are all ultimately dependent on the involvement and competence of the receivers of the communication. The enormous amount of evaluative research in the museum is testimony, of course, to the acceptance of this view. However much of that evaluative work is premised on, at best, an inadequate view of the museum as a medium, and also on an inadequate view of the role of the visitor in contributing to, rather than simply receiving, the communications on offer. I hope that the discussion offered here will help change that.

Acknowledgements

This paper arises from work undertaken as a result of a grant from the Economic and Social Research Council under its Public Understanding of Science programme. The field work for the research was conducted by Dr Sharon Macdonald of Keele University. I would like to thank Dr Macdonald for her generous and challenging comments on an earlier draft of this paper.

Notes and references

1 Macdonald, S, and Silverstone, R, 'Rewriting the museum's fictions: taxonomies, stories and readers', *Cultural Studies*, 4, 2 (1990), pp176-91
   Macdonald, S, and Silverstone, R, 'Science on display: the representation of scientific controversy in museum exhibtions', *Public Understanding of Science*, 1 (1992)
2 Vergo, P (ed), *The New Museology* (London: Reaktion Books, 1989)
3 Lumley, R (ed), *The Museum Time Machine* (London: Routledge, 1988)
   Hewison, R, *The Heritage Industry: Britain in a Climate of Decline* (London: Methuen, 1987)
4 Giddens, A, *The Consequences of Modernity* (Cambridge: Polity Press, 1990)
5 Anderson, B, *Imagined Communities* (London: Verso, 1982)
   Scannell, P, 'Public service broadcasting and modern public life', *Media, Culture and Society*, 11, 2 (1989), pp135-66
6 Kopytoff, I, 'The cultural biography of things: commoditisation as process', in Appadurai, A (ed), *The Social Life of Things: Commodities in Cultural Perspective* (Cambridge: Cambridge University Press, 1986)

7 Saumarez-Smith, C, 'Museums, artefacts and meanings', in Vergo, P (ed), pp6-21

8 Jordanova, L, 'Objects of knowledge: an historical perspective on museums', in Vergo, P (ed), pp22-40

9 Morton, A, 'Tomorrow's yesterdays: science museums and the future', in Lumley, R (ed), pp128-43

10 Eco, U, *Travels in Hyperreality* (London: Picador, 1987)
Baudrillard, J, *For a Critique of the Political Economy of the Sign* (St Louis: Telos Press, 1981)

11 Donato, E, 'The museum's furnace: notes toward a contextual reading of *Bouvard and Pécuchet*', in Josué, H (ed), *Textual Strategies: Perspectives in Post-Structuralist Criticism* (London: Methuen, 1980), p223

12 Stewart, S, *On Longing: Narratives of the Miniature, the Gigantic, the Souvenir, the Collection* (Baltimore and London: John Hopkins University Press)

13 Douglas, M, and Isherwood, B, *The World of Goods* (Harmondsworth: Penguin, 1979)

14 Macdonald, S, and Silverstone, R (1990)

15 Bennett, T, 'Museums and the "people"', in Lumley, R (ed), p63-85

16 Harraway, D, 'Teddy bear patriarchy: taxidertormy in the garden of Eden, New York City, 1908-1936', *Social Text*, 11 (1984-5), p2,064

17 Bud, R, 'The myth and the machine: seeing science through museum eyes', in Fyfe, G, and Law, J (eds), *Picturing Power: Visual Depiction and Social Relations* (London: Routledge, 1988)

18 de Certeau, M, *The Practice of Everyday Life* (Berkeley: California University Press, 1984)

19 Bud, R

20 cf Szenec, J, *Flaubert à l'exposition de 1851*, quoted by Donato, E, p225: 'I am inclined to believe that an object is chosen on account of its special power of evocation. This knick-knack, that accessory, is the fragment of a civilisation, which, by itself, it is capable of suggesting. "Is not all of China contained in a Chinese woman's slipper decorated with damask roses and having embroidered cats on its vamp?" In basing itself on objects, the imagination reconstructs that universe whose quintessence they express.'

21 Macdonald, S, and Silverstone, R (1990)

22 See Macdonald, S, and Silverstone, R (1992)

23 Macdonald, S, 'What is science anyway? Frameworks for understanding among visitors to a science museum exhibition' (forthcoming)

24 Paolozzi, E, *Lost Magic Kingdoms* (London: British Museum, 1985)

25 Mellencamp, P, 'TV time and catastrophe: or beyond the pleasure principle of television', in Mellencamp, P (ed) *Logics of Television* (Bloomington: Indiana University Press, 1990), p240
cf McLuhan, M, *Understanding Media* (London: Routledge, 1964); Goody, J, *The Domestication of the Savage Mind* (Cambridge: Cambridge University Press, 1977); Eisenstein, E, *The Printing Press in an Age of Social Change* (Cambridge: Cambridge University Press, 1979); Ong, W, *Orality and Literacy: The Technologizing of the Word* (London: Methuen, 1982); and Meyrowitz, J, *No Sense of Place: The Impact of Electronic Media on Social Behaviour* (New York and Oxford: Oxford University Press, 1985)

26 cf Ferguson, M, 'Electronic media and the redefining of time and space', in Ferguson, M (ed), *Public Communication: The New Imperatives* (London and Newbury Park: Sage, 1991) pp152-71

27 Kantor, D, and Lehr, W, *Inside the Family* (San Francisco: Jossey-Bass, 1975)
Reiss, D, *The Family's Construction of Reality* (Cambridge, MA: Harvard University Press, 1981)

28 Kantor, D, and Lehr, W, p82

29 cf de Certeau
Silverstone, R, 'Let us then return to the murmurings of everyday practices: a note on Michel de Certeau, television and everyday life', *Theory, Culture and Society*, 6, 1 (1989), pp77-94

30 Macdonald, S, and Silverstone, R (1990)

31 Miles, R, *The Design of Educational Exhibits* (London: Unwin Hyman, 2nd ed, 1988)

32 cf Bud, R

33 Silverstone, R, 'From audiences to consumers: the household and the consumption of communication and information technologies', *European Journal of Communication*, 6, 2 (1991), pp135-54

34 Winnicott, D, *From Playing to Reality* (Harmondsworth: Penguin, 1974)

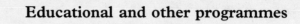

Educational and other programmes

Drama on the galleries

Graham Farmelo

Over lunch the other day, a distinguished curator remarked to me: 'Whenever I see an actor hamming it up on a gallery, my flesh creeps'. She complained that, 'objects speak for themselves, so there's really no need for all this megaphone museology'.

As my companion prodded disconsolately at her *fettucine spinaci*, lamenting what she believed to be the passing primacy of the object, my heart went out to her. She is plainly shocked to see her beloved museum (in the north country) change so rapidly from its former role as a shrine for historical artefacts, with visitors allowed to file by reverentially at the convenience of the staff. Now, she believes, the quietly beating heart of the museum is being torn out by new interpretive techniques of which drama is only one: there are also the hands-on exhibits and displays, audio guides, gallery demonstrations, videos, electronically controlled slide shows and so on. The humble label is now seen more often than not as a quaint afterthought, there only to appease the experts.

A new interpretive technique

It is hardly surprising that these new interpretive techniques have come to the fore over the last two decades. All the ingredients for change were there, notably: the increasing competition from other media (especially TV and video, which cater so readily for the five-minute attention span); the availability of new technology at gradually decreasing costs; and increasing demands from funding agencies that museums should give visitors what they want. There has been a gradual and regrettable shift away from reverence for scholarship for its own sake, although, in the academics' retreat, there has been a welcome drive towards greater efforts to communicate their work to the public.

Gallery drama is probably the most low tech of the new interpretive methods used in museums. The technique may be seen as an elaboration of the art of the country-house guide, although, in my view, it is more accurate to regard gallery drama as a descendant of street theatre, which originated in Roman times.[1] A pioneering institution was the Science Museum of Minnesota in the USA, which began in the early 1970s to use character cameos as a way of interpreting some of its exhibits.[2] The programme, which initially involved actors giving monologues and demonstrations, was from the outset popular with visitors, and it grew steadily, to the extent that the Museum established a theatre department in 1984. Their programme is now implemented by a director, actors (four full-time, one part-time), playwrights commissioned for individual pieces, and design staff responsible for the sets and lighting.

The Minnesota project has been profoundly influential. Museums – notoriously political institutions – now have drama on the galleries as well as behind them. Over the last 20 years, many drama projects have sprouted in museums, notably in Europe and in North America.[3] In the UK, the Science Museum in London has led the way in the use of drama to interpret topics in science, technology and medicine. This venture began as an experiment in 1987 with a single actor and there is now a daily drama programme provided by a company of 19 actors who perform about 20 roles, most of which are associated with specific exhibits.[4]

Many ways have been found of implementing gallery drama. In their daily programme of events, some museums present several short (10-minute) small-scale monologues or dialogues, while others choose to give fewer, comparatively long (30- to 40-minute) presentations involving several actors (or even entire companies). Some institutions encourage audiences to keep their distance, whereas others strive to achieve close involvement between the visitors and the performers. Some adopt an informal approach to the preparation of the actors' pieces (many of which are virtually extemporised around a well-researched brief), others use carefully prepared scripts from which deviation is discouraged. The topics sometimes concern individual exhibits, but they often relate to a whole gallery or even to the entire museum.[5]

Why drama?

Why is that exhibit important? How does it work? Who drove it? Where was it used? What were its social and economic consequences? None of these questions crosses the minds of many of the Science Museum's visitors who pass Stephenson's *Rocket*, yet it is a veritable icon of British industrial culture, which is why it is featured on the back of the five pound note. Any indifference on the part of the visitors is challenged, and usually dispelled, when an actor is working alongside the locomotive, playing Samuel Smiles (Stephenson's biographer). A connection is made entertainingly – in a non-didactic way – between an inanimate object and the human audience by another person. To my mind, this 'human factor' is a crucial reason for the popularity and effectiveness of gallery drama: no other interpretive technique can make these links in this way.

The emotional responses of audiences to actors performing on museum galleries are often a joy to behold: how many of the visitors would have been as affected by a label or, for that matter, by an audio or video presentation? Moreover, an actor can change his or her performance to suit the spectators. By skilfully modifying the basic content of the presentation, it is possible to engage the attention of the wide-eyed young child, the cynical teenager (often the hardest nut to crack), and the uninterested adult, all at the same time. This is usually beyond the scope of the gallery video, which conveys a single message which has more often than not been enfeebled by the makers' attempts to cater for every sector of the visiting public. By trying to offend no one, everyone is disappointed. It is hardly surprising that videos have not proved to be a very compelling way of attracting the attention of visitors.

It is even possible for the actor to achieve that most difficult of feats for museums, the communication of several interpretations of a single object or idea. The character can do this, for example, by suggesting that he or she believes one thing, while others have completely different views. Strategic nodding and winking can be an effective way of indicating that none of the interpretations is necessarily correct.

Actors on museum galleries have to strike a balance between their roles as educators and entertainers: they should neither be purely one nor the other. In order to communicate some difficult idea or concept, it is sometimes necessary to be didactic, temporarily playing down the lighter side of the performance. On the other hand, actors sometimes have to play the clown in order to hold their audience. This flexibility is one of the most important weapons in the actors' armoury, because it affords a way of maintaining the interest of the visitors. It helps to explain why, compared with third-person interpretation (scripted demonstrations), character actors have been found to be significantly more compelling for audiences.[6]

An unalloyed benefit?

Although the introduction of museum drama is widely perceived to be a success, my lunchtime companion is not the only one who is sceptical of its benefits.[7] A common objection is that this method of interpretation is particularly invasive: it tends to take over the surrounding area in the gallery, in much the same way that a television dominates a living room. In these days of remote control, TVs can be switched off at will but alas, *Star Trek* is still science fiction, so the visitor who does not want to see actors performing cannot simply beam them up to another gallery.

Even the most discreet performance has the effect of changing the atmosphere of a gallery. Some would argue that it comes alive, others complain that the magical quiet of the museum is destroyed. Holden Caulfield would surely have agreed with them. In praising the Museum of Natural History in New York, he noted approvingly that it was a place in which 'everything always stayed right where it was'. Caulfield liked the Museum because it remained the same, enabling him to gauge changes to himself: 'Nobody'd be different. The only thing that would be different would be *you*'.[8] Sentimental this attitude may be, but museum directors ignore it at their peril.

It is probably not these conservative objections that deter museums from expanding (or initiating) drama programmes: the most important constraint is financial. Thomas Agnotti was quite correct when he asserted more than a decade ago that 'the resources required to train performers and develop entertainment that is historically valid are normally not available to museums'.[9]

Actors normally require payment, and, like most human beings, they cost more than the machines (such as videos) that could replace them. Moreover, machines do not catch colds, ask for pay rises, or suffer from stage fright. Nor do they need props and a Green Room. Much more important, once a dramatic piece has been prepared and edited for a video presentation, it can be guaranteed that every visitor can see the same performance. It remains only to ensure that the machine is properly maintained; with the advent of digital technology, even the quality of the sound and picture are undiminished by time.

It is normally regarded as bad practice to fetter actors with precisely worded scripts, leaving them unable to improvise performances to suit the audience. The danger of this strategy is of course that the outline script tends to change week by week, and that emphases are gradually altered to please audiences at the expense of what might be called 'interpretive balance'. Factual errors can also creep in: apocrypha appear, dates change, scientific inaccuracies intrude, and so on. This is only to be expected: after all, actors are only human. The only way to avoid this is by investing in what industrialists call 'quality control'. It is essential that regular checks are made to ensure that the performances of a role maintain the balance and accuracy that they had when it was first approved. This is an essential and expensive overhead to the cost of any programme of gallery drama if it is to be properly administered.

These difficulties have deterred some museums from embarking on large-scale drama programmes. However, the interpretive technique is now well established, as a result of its effectiveness and its wide popularity, particularly with children.[10] Very few museums have problems in attracting audiences for their drama events. On the contrary, the presence of actors often tends to attract visitors away from other parts of the museum, causing congestion in the performance areas. How many other interpretive techniques can boast such success?

What next?

The Holden Caulfields of the museum world – including my lunch-time companion – are on the defensive. For museums, perennially strapped for cash and unable to afford refurbishments, the introduction of drama programmes has offered a popular and relatively inexpensive way of freshening up tired galleries. The world of science, also traditionally short of funds, is now looking to open its doors to a wider audience.[11] How can the success of museum drama be developed and what is its untapped potential for promoting the public awareness of science? The following gives a few ideas.

Given the popularity of drama with school visitors, it makes sense to develop versions of roles that are particularly relevant to subjects being pursued in the classroom. The non-didactic nature of the best drama presentations allows them to communicate messages that are difficult to teach in other ways. Perhaps, for example, there would be some potential in organising meetings between teachers and those involved in gallery presentations, in order to identify potential target topics. The introduction of the national curriculum has ensured that the problem areas encountered by teachers in state schools all over the country are broadly similar, so local meetings between drama staff and teachers should furnish material relevant to other state schools.

It may be possible to involve teachers (and trainee teachers) in the production of gallery drama, for example when topics are being decided and when scripts are being prepared. This would deepen the teachers' appreciation of the technique, encourage them to visit gallery drama events with their pupils and also help them to build on the experience of the visits when they are back in the classroom. Similarly, there may be scope for this type of involvement on the part of adult education groups.

Many museums have reserve collections of objects that, for one reason or another, are dispensable, and so can be handled with impunity by the public. Such collections are often used by school groups to obtain hands-on experience of the objects. Perhaps more could be made of these collections by gallery actors, enabling visitors to share in the handling of the props, possibly during performances.

Visitors (from schools and from the public) often comment that the most vivid memories of a museum are those relating to a gallery performance seen during a visit.[12] It may well be worthwhile to produce associated educational materials. With the aid of flexible electronic publishing techniques, it should be a simple matter to adapt material in order to produce separate versions for the specialist, for the family group, for each key stage of the national curriculum, etc. (It is tempting to suggest that associated video material should also be produced, but, alas, live drama events are normally killed in attempts to preserve them on film).

Visitor-flow problems are often the most irksome consequences of a successful gallery presentation. One way to anticipate these difficulties is to design new galleries with a view to accommodating performing actors and to storing props. This must be done with some subtlety in order to preserve something of the magical transformation that occurs when part of a museum is temporarily transformed into a theatre. A theatre built separately within a museum would isolate the drama, destroying the unusual quality it gives to the collections of objects on the galleries.

How can the quality of the scripts be improved? This is a considerable challenge: it is unlikely that many top-flight playwrights could be persuaded to write for museum drama groups if they were aware that their expertly crafted words would be abandoned at the drop of a hat to cater for the vagaries of an audience. However, the rewards of persuading professional writers to work with museums could be considerable. If Tom Stoppard can write an entertaining play addressing some of the fundamentals of quantum mechanics, one relishes the thought of what he would make of the equally recondite subject matter of some museums.[13]

As museums become more professional in their management, market-research techniques are increasingly used to monitor the audience's reaction to 'the product'. There are two ways in which this can be used to benefit gallery drama programmes. First, it is likely that such research will demonstrate the sheer popularity of this interpretive technique, which will consequently be better placed to bid for increased funds for development, and, just as important, for quality control. Second, the success of an individual role can be evaluated in order to try and see how it can be improved or, occasionally, whether it should be dropped. The art of evaluating drama in this way is in its infancy and it will be a quite a challenge to use the data sensitively and constructively. Anyone who attempts to evaluate an art form is always vulnerable to rhetorical questions of the type, 'How can you mark a sunny day out of 10?' This is a legitimate objection, but it must surely be possible to develop some way of gauging the popularity and effectiveness of a dramatic piece. One thing is certain: the evaluation must not be left (as so often happens in practice) to the actors and to those closely associated with the programme. That is akin to asking a company and its director to write a review of their own performance.

Is it feasible to arrange collaborations between museums which are currently arranging drama programmes? Such a venture would help museums to share scripts, audience feedback, evaluation data, training facilities, props and so on. Also, it could assist museums which have not begun to use drama in the early stages, so that they do not have to re-invent the wheel. This is the kind of idea that is overwhelmingly approved in principle at meetings and conferences, but that subsequently withers and dies owing to a lack of both commitment and resources. The rewards for collaborative ventures could be considerable, but first it will be necessary for an organisation to take the lead and for finances to be made available by contributing museums.

Finally, drama programmes are labour intensive and therefore expensive. It may be possible for two or more museums to overcome this perennial difficulty by sharing a company of actors, a director and the administrative burden.

The actor as scientist

One innovation in gallery drama at the Science Museum in London proved particularly successful last year. In the exhibition presented to commemorate the bicentenary of the birth of Michael Faraday, actors played the role of the great scientist four times (or more) each day for the seven-month duration of the exhibition. The role was a gift, as Faraday was a warm and complex personality, the doyen of Victorian lecturers, and one of the originators of the public understanding of science movement. Moreover, his life is extremely well documented.[14]

These performances proved to be very popular with the visitors (although not quite as popular as the exhibition's interactives).[15] An enclosed area of the gallery was set aside for the actor and his audience, and it was in this part of the exhibition that Faraday's enquiring spirit and love of informative and entertaining demonstrations (particularly directed towards children) came across vividly to the audience. In addition, he was even able to make posthumous contributions to public lectures about his life, courtesy of his impersonators.

Not all great scientists can be truthfully portrayed as engaging characters. However, as experience with the Faraday role has demonstrated, if such a portrayal is valid, the technique is very powerful. The audience sees that science is not a list of intimidating abstractions in a textbook: it is the imaginative product of personalities who rarely conform to the stereotype of an egghead with a white coat.

Postscript

These are hard times for both science and museums. Scientists are, perhaps, keener than ever to promote their message to non-specialists – to encourage the public understanding of science.

Similarly, museums are now striving harder than ever to open their doors to a wider public, in order to encourage more visitors to enjoy their collections. Drama is a potent form of interpretation that has the potential to communicate a wide range of ideas in and about science to audiences that may be put off by more formal educational methods. It is traditional – and wise – to be sceptical of the power of the tools of art to communicate science. Gallery drama is, however, an exception to the rule.

Notes and references

1 Harwood, R, *All the World's a Stage* (London: Martin, Secker & Warburg 1984)

2 Quinn, S, and Bedworth, J, 'Science theatre: an effective interpretive technique in museums', *Communicating Science to the Public* (Chichester: Wiley, 1987), pp161-74
Quinn, S, 'Theatre techniques as a method of interpretation for adults', *Museums, Adults and the Humanities: a Guide for Educational Programming* (Washington DC, 1981), pp257-70

3 Alsford, S, and Parry, D, 'Interpretive theatre: a role in museums?' *Museum Management and Curatorship*, 10 (1991), pp8-23

4 Richardson, P, 'History: the human factor', in *Museums and Galleries 1992* (East Grinstead: British Leisure Publications)

5 Alsford, S, and Parry, D

6 Quinn, S

7 Dickenson, V, 'What are museums for?', *Canadian Forum* (February 1990), pp18-21

8 Salinger, J D, *The Catcher in the Rye* (Harmondsworth: Penguin Books, 1951) p127

9 Agnotti, T, 'Planning the open-air museum and teaching urban history: the United States in the world context' *Museum*, 32 (1982), p183

10 Forbes, M, 'Museum theatre in a children's museum', *Journal of Museum Education*, 15 (1985), pp2-18

11 Bodmer, W, *The Public Understanding of Science* (London: Royal Society, 1985)

12 Quinn, S

13 Stoppard, T, *Hapgood* (London: Faber and Faber, 1988)

14 Cantor, G, *Michael Faraday: Sandemanian and Scientist* (Basingstoke: Macmillan, 1991)

15 Bicknell, S, *et al*, *Evaluation of the exhibition Michael Faraday and the modern world*, (Science Museum internal report, 1991)

Providing information, promoting understanding

Leonard Will

Should museums have information services?

If you want to see objects and press buttons, go to a science museum; if you want scientific information, go to a library. So runs the conventional wisdom, but it is changing. Museums have an ambiguous role: they aim to provide culture, entertainment and education in an integrated way, with each type of experience enhancing the other. In many ways these roles are also true for libraries, and there is now an encouraging rapprochement between the two types of institution.

Both museums and libraries try to encourage people to make use of their services, by giving the impression of being welcoming, interesting places, where a user will find an enjoyable and enriching experience. Both feel that they are not just catering to an existing demand, but that it is their public responsibility to create a demand for a product which the public do not know they want. This product is not only knowledge, but also understanding: a change of attitude towards the subject being presented.

Libraries have had this goal for many years, but no matter how imaginative their displays and leaflets, and no matter how attractive the book covers, there is no denying that a picture of a space capsule, say, has nothing like the impact of seeing the real thing. Museums are not only able to present 'real things' but they can also put them into context and allow a visitor to enter the world where the objects are used.

The content of displays is generally determined by museum staff: they decide what the public will find interesting. On the contrary, information services primarily respond to enquiries from users. A museum visitor with a question may approach anyone who appears to be a member of staff, particularly if that person seems to have responsibility for dealing with the public, such as a warder or someone on duty at a reception or information desk. That member of staff may be able to answer the question personally, or they may decide to pass it on. They then have to decide whether the appropriate destination is a curator, the library, the education service, the marketing department, the administration or another institution altogether. The same decisions have to be made by switchboard operators for telephone enquiries, and by registry staff for letters. The result is often very inconsistent, with the quality of the response depending more on chance than on museum policy.

An exciting symbiosis is developing, where different sections of museums are working together in a mutually dependent relationship to provide an integrated service to visitors unaware of the divisions between the library, the curatorial, and the interpretive functions. The unifying theme is 'information'; this may be information about objects in the collections, or about topics in the general subject area covered by the institution. The aim is to provide a single point of approach and to draw on whichever of the institution's resources are most appropriate to deal with the enquirer's need.

Several museums, including the Science Museum, have been moving towards integration. The National Maritime Museum in Greenwich has set up a Maritime Information Centre, staffed by library and curatorial staff; a similar integrated service is provided in the Prins Hendrik Maritime Museum in Rotterdam; and an information centre is planned as a central focus of the new Museum of Scotland being built by the National Museums of Scotland in Edinburgh.

Services in the Science Museum

In the Science Museum we have run two experimental integrated information services, and we are now comparing the results of these with a general survey of the way in which we handle enquiries, in order to plan for an enhanced service in the future.

Food and nutrition information service

Our first service was on food and nutrition, and was launched as a telephone 'hot-line' service at the opening of the new *Food for thought* gallery in the autumn of 1989. We set up a special telephone number and staffed it between the hours of 10:00 and 16:00. Outside these times an answering machine explained that the service hours were limited: this meant that staff had time to work on answering enquiries and building up information resources. We limited the number of enquiries received by providing only one line, because we did not wish the service to spill over and prevent other staff from dealing with the general enquiry work of the library. The information service staff took over the resource files which had been built up by curators while the gallery was being planned and developed; many of these files contained brochures and advisory leaflets produced by relevant organisations, including government departments. We also had a collection of reference books and textbooks, and a file of contact names and telephone numbers in other organisations.

Two main lessons were learned from this experiment. Firstly, staff who were not specialists in the subject, but who had a general background in science, technology and information work, were able to provide helpful answers to the great majority of the questions asked. They did not necessarily provide a definitive answer to every question, and indeed it was not intended that they should. In providing the service to help promote the public understanding of science and technology, we were keen to promote the idea that scientists in white coats do not have all the answers, and that there are disagreements within the world of science. Food and nutrition was a topic relevant to the public where this point could be very clearly made. The public are presented with so much publicity about food, from organisations with various partial points of view, that it seemed possible that they might see the Science Museum as presenting an authoritative and neutral voice able to tell the perplexed citizen what is really the truth. Of course we could not take the role of either advocate or judge; our job was to present the data as well as we could ascertain it, with a clear indication of where it came from, and to try to explain the conclusions which were drawn. The intention was to put the enquirer in a better position to decide which argument seemed most convincing.

Secondly, enquirers did not retain details of a service of this type, but used it if it was drawn to their attention at the moment when they had a question on their mind. We did not advertise the service, but included it in the press releases which we distributed for the opening of the *Food for*

thought gallery, and it was mentioned several times in the press and on radio interviews by the Head of our Division, John Durant. Each time the service was publicised it attracted a flurry of questions, but these tailed off within a few days. It seems clear that continuous publicity is needed to keep people aware of a service of this kind, at least until it becomes common knowledge. Paid publicity is expensive, but there are considerable opportunities for editorial coverage in the media so long as the service has something topical and interesting to say. A pro-active approach with information and background on current events both keeps the service in the public eye and also enhances its status as being up to date and concerned with the present rather than the past.

As the service was experimental, however, we were not able to develop the possibilities for long-term publicity, and we did not attempt to continue its promotion after demand had dropped to a negligible amount. Any questions we receive on this topic are now dealt with in the normal way by the general enquiries service provided by the Library.

Science information service

This was a more ambitious service, aimed at visitors to the Science Museum. In one of the galleries we set up a staffed enquiry desk in front of an area, defined by display panels, which contained the service's resources: tables and chairs for visitors; popular science books; encyclopedias and quick reference books; a microcomputer with a colour display, used to search an encyclopedia and indexes to current general science publications on compact disc (CD-ROM); a terminal for accessing the Museum's central computer databases of objects and library stock; and displays of press cuttings and information sheets on topical issues.

It was staffed by 'general practitioner' scientists, information scientists, and curators, who were able to talk through questions with visitors and either provide them with information from their own resources or put them in touch with specialists from the staff of the Museum or elsewhere. A major aim was again to provide explanations rather than just facts, to help people to understand the limits of what we know and to realise that opinions are only as good as the data on which they are based.

Two staff were on duty at any one time, and as

the service was available throughout the Museum's opening hours, including weekends, the total staffing was the equivalent of four full-time posts. Because of the substantial staff cost, the Museum was able to fund the service only for an experimental period of three months in the spring of 1991. We are now planning the form which a continuation of the service should take.

Visitors who used the service liked it. They found the staff friendly, helpful and knowledgeable, and they were impressed with the information provided. Over 95 per cent of people who asked for help were satisfied with the answers they were given. The number of visitors who used the service was, however, smaller than we had hoped. The service dealt with 6,191 visitors. Of these enquiries 60 per cent were directional, 6 per cent were educational, and the remaining 34 per cent were users of the service's scientific and technical resources, half by self-service and half by asking the staff for help and information. The service operated for 87 days, and the average number of users per day was thus 71, of whom 24 users were seeking scientific or technical information. The staff were not fully occupied in dealing with enquiries and could have dealt with more.

Many enquiries were from teachers and children. The teachers often used it to help them plan visits to the Museum, and indeed the service incorporated the services otherwise provided by a separate teacher information desk, including distribution of packs prepared by our Education Service. Children were often prompted by their parents to come and ask questions – sometimes, we felt, because the parents did not know the answers but thought that an admission of ignorance would come more acceptably from a child.

Many visitors, however, did not want to spend time talking or reading: they had paid to see the exhibits, and wanted to make the most of that time. Visitors often come for an outing, with no particular information-gathering objective, and they want the museum to put interesting things before them, rather than their being expected to have an agenda of questions. In retrospect, then, it seems that a service based in the museum itself would not tap a high proportion of the latent demand throughout the country.

We concluded, therefore, that two things had to be done. Firstly, we have to improve our way of handling the enquiries which *do* come to the Museum, by integrating the enquiry services provided by our several divisions – curators, library, education, marketing and warding staff – so that however a member of the public approaches us their enquiry is fed into a system which ensures that it is dealt with promptly, efficiently, and at the right level. A survey and assessment of this possibility is now under way.

Secondly, we should explore the possibility of setting up and publicising a national science and technology information service, to provide a service to the general public by letter and telephone as well as by personal visit. This is an ambitious project which will need more resources than the Science Museum can provide, but we hope to move forward by co-operating with other organisations to share the work and the cost. Such a service would not attempt to meet the information needs of professional scientists and technologists, which are already provided for by academic, professional, commercial and national libraries and information services.

A vision of the future

A future science information service will have a wide range of resources to choose from. The core requirement must still be staff who are able to talk through a question, and who have a sufficient knowledge of science and technology to understand the background and explain fundamentals, in a manner which is encouraging and not intimidating.

They will be backed up by a wide range of information resources, both printed, and, increasingly, electronic. These will include reference and bibliographical materials, of the kind which we used in our experimental projects, but the service will also continue to put enquirers in touch with people who can help them more, drawing both on the expertise within the Museum and from the whole world outside. Electronic mailing systems and retrieval of information from external databanks will be extensively used, with images and perhaps sound as well as text. The service will also build up its own database of sources used and information assembled when dealing with enquiries, which will develop in a direction determined by demand. This database will be accessible to, and added to by, all staff who deal with enquiries, and it will also provide the administrative control to ensure that service quality is maintained.

An enquiry may still be best answered by talking it through, and by providing a publication, a photocopy, or an information sheet, but it will also be possible to provide an interactive experience, either simulated, using anything from a video disk to a virtual reality system, or actual, by taking the enquirer to a gallery where they can see and perhaps try out the real thing.

An information service is one way in which a museum can fulfil a national role, despite being physically based in one city, and as mentioned above, it may well be used more by people who do not visit the museum in person than by those who do. The role of the staff as mediators then becomes even more important, because they have to search for and choose materials on behalf of enquirers who cannot browse for themselves. Replies will often be composed in the traditional way, but the staff will be helped by easy access to databases of the resources of their own institution and of others, and kept up-to-date by a continual inflow of information about current scientific and technical events. Remote on-line access to the catalogues of most UK university libraries is already widely available, and many museum catalogues are likely to follow suit. Increasingly members of the public will be able to access these resources from their homes, and museum staff will spend more time analysing and synthesising information to make it both retrievable and digestible.

The museum information service of 20 years from now may not be highly visible, perhaps because it will be so pervasive that it is indistinguishable from the museum itself.

Access to image: a schools programme for special needs

Janet Hill

During 1991, the National Museum of Photography, Film and Television in Bradford worked with IN-VALID? – Bradford's disability arts group – to present the project *Access to image*. The project explored image making by disabled photographers, and provided a starting point for disabled people to explore issues of disability and representation through practical photography and discussion.

The schools programme was initiated by the seconded teacher to the Museum, as part of the *Access to image* project. The programme was initially intended to reflect the philosophy and content of the project, but when it became apparent that this was not entirely appropriate, the parameters were altered to facilitate access to the Museum's Education Unit, and to its interactive learning resources and approaches. The target groups were extended to include pupils and students with a wide range of special educational needs, not just those with disabilities. For pupils to gain the most benefit, it was seen as important to target teachers, and to have a strong in-service training element to the programme. All schools, colleges, and social education centres within easy reach of Bradford that provide education for people with special needs were contacted. The response rate was high.

The schools programme aimed to present examples of good educational practice which would provide a starting point for teachers to develop their skills. These examples were to be delivered through active learning workshops. Teachers were to be involved in the whole process starting at the planning stage. The visual medium was to be used as a tool to support active learning, and as a means to identify processes by which teachers could foster their pupils' language, communication, personal, and social skills. The provision of a well-resourced and highly motivating learning environment at the NMPFT was to enable teachers to experience the value of active learning approaches. The processes and skills involved could then be transferred to other learning situations.

The rationale for emphasising access to the active learning resources at the Museum was based on the fact that many teachers of pupils with special educational needs already use active, experiential learning as a primary method of delivering the curriculum. This approach is recognised as a route to developing independence, self-awareness and assertiveness in pupils, as well as supporting cross-curricular skills such as problem solving, communication, and co-operation. The approach supports skill transference and learning outside school within the community.

The teacher's role in active learning is crucial: he or she becomes a facilitator for learning, not a didactic instructor. Active learning gives teachers the opportunity to create a relaxed but stimulating environment, where pupils learn at their own pace, and where frustration is reduced to a minimum. Many young people with learning difficulties, special educational needs, and disabilities have a very poor self image, become quickly frustrated in their efforts to learn, and are easily disaffected by school. Active learning can be immensely satisfying, rewarding and motivating. It can lead to dramatic improvements in behaviour and confidence. It is very much an enabling process for both pupils and teachers.

The resources selected for use during the programme included a working mock-up of a TV studio; a well-equipped photography studio with a large darkroom; and equipment such as cameras and video camcorders which could be used outside the Museum either at the pupils' own school, or in the community.

In most cases, it was possible to suggest workshops based around work already happening in school, and to cover attainment targets in various subjects of the national curriculum, notably English, technology, and science.

One workshop involved a group of pupils with learning difficulties who used English as a second language. These children were all from a mainstream middle school. Year seven pupils were working on a project called *Change in our Environment*, and were looking particularly at the locality of the school. The special educational needs co-ordinator at the school wanted a group of children from the year with the greatest learning difficulties to undertake a project which would improve their self esteem and raise their status with the peer group. She had not originally thought of using the year group project as the basis for a workshop, but once the possibility was raised, she became extremely enthusiastic.

It was decided that the group would use cameras to take photographs of the local environment as part of their project work, and then choose some of the negative contact prints for enlarging. Cameras were taken to the school, where the children learned how to use them, and then took them out into the locality. The children then came to the Museum to enlarge the chosen images using the darkroom. The main part of the project, however, was to design, plan and make a video about a local mill, once the workplace of many of the children's relatives, but which was now disused. The mill is to be converted into a museum, a hotel and an office complex in the near future. The children made a visual statement about the changes taking place.

The children were taught to use a video camera and tripod, and with this and the now familiar 'point and shoot' cameras, recorded a visit to the mill. They worked on the script and documentary in the TV studio at the Museum, using their own still images as backgrounds. The final edited documentary used all the pupils' own work with the video camera, their still photography, sound effects and script. The finished work was displayed at the school, and shown to other pupils and parents.

Other workshops were clearly 'one-off' visits, partly due to travelling distances. One teacher wanted to bring a group of nine- to ten-year-old children with behavioural and emotional difficulties for a 'trial' workshop at the Museum. All those in the group had been excluded from mainstream schools: their teacher explained that their presenting behaviours resulted from seriously disturbed backgrounds. One child, for example, had recently witnessed a murder in the family. Another had tried to commit suicide twice, and all had been the victims of physical or sexual abuse. Presenting behaviours ranged from a refusal to take part in activities, through very short attention span and restlessness, to extremely disruptive behaviour. She was worried that a workshop would be refused on the grounds of the childrens' behaviour, and was very anxious to assure all concerned that the children would benefit. She had no idea what she

wanted the group to achieve, thinking only that she wanted something that would enhance the children's self image, and support oral language and listening skills. The children had never used photography before.

It was decided that a project with immediate results and a high level of impact with the children, using practical activity as a tool to support self image and communication skills, was the way forward. The project was given the name *Mugshots*. The process involved a preliminary team-building session to enable co-operative working and communication, followed by brainstorming and discussion around the idea of self image and representation. This led into studying ways of producing visual images or *Mugshots*. Polaroid cameras were used in small groups by the children to create visual portrait images of each other. Because of the immediate feedback, the activity generated considerable excitement and discussion. After about 30 minutes, a second activity was introduced. The children designed and made individual photograms intended to complement the polaroid portraits. These were imaginary portrait images of themselves using any objects that appealed to them or had some personal significance. The photograms were mounted together with individual photographs to create a *Mugshot* image. The workshop ended with the children sharing their experiences.

The teacher was very excited at the way the children had worked co-operatively and successfully as a group ('a very rare occurrence') and about the high level of positive behaviour, concentration, and communication achieved during the workshop. She was keen to continue using active learning in school, and also to organise another workshop at the Museum.

These are only two examples of workshops within the schools programme. Other groups taking part included young people with physical disabilities, complex and multiple difficulties, learning and social difficulties. In fact, they were not all children or young people: the eldest workshop participant was 64!

Access difficulties were encountered by one or two groups, largely due to a combination of unsuitable building design, circumstance and group numbers. Resource difficulties were highlighted by problems handling equipment, and lack of space in some areas.

It was clear that the *Access to image* programme

created a welcome opportunity for targeted groups to obtain easy access to the Museum and to the Education facilities in particular. Most teachers commented that they had not thought of using the Museum with groups before, because they had thought that the facilities were not suitable or available for use with special needs groups.

Evaluation of the programme indicated that teachers were excited by the potential of using visual media technology and active learning in curriculum development, particularly for language development and communication skills. They saw the approach as a teaching tool for themselves and a tool for pupils. They were keen to develop the skills and processes they had used in the workshops further.

Teachers were highly motivated by pupils' positive responses. The best testimonial to the success of the schools programme came from the children and young people taking part. One girl commented, 'I haven't done any work today, but I feel tired out!' Another youngster said, 'Can we come again tomorrow? I enjoyed that!'

What more is there to say?

Linking scientists to non-science museums

Patrick Sudbury

There are over 2,000 museums and galleries in the UK dealing with every subject imaginable. Although only some of these museums and galleries are directly concerned with science, all are fertile ground for developing public awareness of the science underlying their subject matter. Often, all that is lacking is the necessary expertise to make the latent science accessible in an interesting and enjoyable way. This paper explores some of the possibilities and limitations of using non-science collections to increase the public understanding of science and cites examples of ways in which this has already been done in some institutions.

Why use museums and galleries?

Museums and galleries are perceived by many as the recorders of our cultural traditions. If people want to know something about a locality, an object, or a living thing, they are likely to consider a visit to the local museum. Museums hold the material evidence that reflects the activities and ecology of the past to the people of today and tomorrow. The public may assume that the evidence selected, shown, and interpreted by museum experts is somehow of greater significance than items omitted or facts not recorded. In this way museums and galleries act as an influence on public opinion and taste and help to shape our culture.

If science and technology are not seen to have played a part in human history and art they may be perceived as of little relevance to our future.[1] This would be as dangerous to our future as it is untrue of our past. There is, therefore, a need to state the role of science and technology in most aspects of human existence. This is, perhaps, the strongest reason for trying to increase the representation of science within our general museums and galleries.

There is also the power of the medium. Museums and galleries in the UK receive about 70 million visits each year. Visitors include 30 per cent of the adult population of the country and a large proportion of those still at school. Most museums and galleries are actively looking for ways to attract the current non-visitors and attendances of 100 million per year are possible by the year 2000. Surveys suggest that many visitors have educational, as well as social and recreational, aims for their visit. There is thus a ready market for scientific ideas particularly if presented in a simple and entertaining way.

The use of existing institutions is cost effective. The cost of running museums and galleries in the UK is estimated at about £350 million per year. Some £200 million is spent on national institutions and the armed services museums, over £125 million on local authority museums, and £25 million on private sector museums.[2] Tapping in to this resource must make more financial sense than duplicating the costs of staff, buildings, and services by building new museums or science centres.

The extra cost of selling scientific ideas within conventional non-scientific museums may seem small but it is nevertheless significant to the institutions themselves. Most museums are struggling to maintain their opening times, their collection care, and their schools programmes.[3] The time, energy, and space required to reflect science in their public displays may well conflict with the use of the same resources for conventional displays. Relatively small sums of 'new' money can act as a catalyst for change. Once the changes have been achieved the operating costs form part of the general overheads of the institution. The examples given below show remarkable results for a very small initial outlay.

Promoting science through general museums allows the full use of the collections unique to each museum and gallery. Technology Testbed in Liverpool was a very successful science hands-on centre. There is no doubt that it derived benefit from the collection items held in the same space. Collections are an amazing resource for creative interpretation. Education officers in museums have been interpreting and making connections between art, history, and science for years and the national curriculum now encourages this approach. It is still necessary, however, to make the cross-curricular links available to all – not just school classes and not just in directly taught sessions.

In summary, there are strategic, marketing, and economic reasons for introducing science to general museums and galleries. There is already experience in museums of making cross-curricular links between art, history, and science. We now have to adapt those links to a public without a trained teacher in its midst.

How should a general museum or gallery reflect science?

One of the greatest barriers to the public understanding of science seems to be its perceived obscurity. Science, we learn, is a word which in its broadest sense is synonymous with learning and knowledge (Latin *scire*: to learn or to know). However, a narrower description such as 'knowledge ascertained by observation and experiment, critically tested and brought under general principles' seems to be more helpful. The idea of technology as 'the practice, description, and terminology of any of the applied sciences of commercial value' seems to reflect its links with science quite explicitly.

Although the organisation sponsoring this publication, the Committee on the Public Understanding of Science (COPUS), suggests that understanding, 'to comprehend, to grasp with the mind, to be fully aware, to follow the logic, meaning, etc', is a main aim, this seems rather a tall order for an untrained public and teachers with limited understanding of science. However COPUS has other goals: 'COPUS aims to provide a focus for a broad-ranging programme to improve public awareness of science and technology'.[4] The use of the term awareness (to be informed, to be conscious of something) seems much more readily achievable in a museum context and at primary schools.

An immediate problem faced by many staff in museums and galleries is recognising the level of scientific literacy that it is reasonable to expect from the public. The headings of the 17 attainment targets in science in the national curriculum (as it was) give some guidance.[5] They are supported by schedules, examples, and programmes of study. However, they are at a level of complexity and detail that it is difficult for those outside the field of formal education to follow. They also stretch the scientific knowledge of some primary school teachers.

The working model used during the 1980s to assess performance in primary schools is also complex but slightly more helpful. The Assessment of Performance Unit (APU) assessed children in primary schools in terms of their understanding of processes and concepts; the context of processes; the deployment of concepts; and their attitudes (see tables 1, 2 and 3 on pages 63 and 64). Thus, the performance assessment of schoolchildren at the age of 11 was based on the expectation that they would acquire some of the basic skills of a scientist (the processes) and understand the basic relationships between life, matter, and forces (the concepts). There was also a hope that they would develop a curiosity and a desire to find out about things from a scientific standpoint (the attitudes). In short, it was expected that our primary school children by the age of 11 would have acquired a basic knowledge and understanding of several branches of science and would have practised some of the skills required of a working scientist.[6]

The APU expectation of primary school children seems to extend far beyond the level of understanding of science it is reasonable to expect of the public in the culture of today. The national curriculum in science may eventually deliver 16-year olds with a satisfactory level of knowledge and understanding but unless that learning is reinforced throughout adult life it will be lost to the individual within a few years. Does COPUS expect all adults to know about the processes and concepts of science? Or are we simply looking for a positive attitude to science? In my view, it is the last of these things that is the most important and it is to changes in attitude that museums can contribute most.

The nature of the museum experience is significant here. The museum visit requires effort on behalf of the visitor who accordingly looks for some reward. Visitors are receptive when they enter a museum or gallery. The opportunity to sell ideas is awaiting the scientist. However, the scientist needs to be aware of the nature of a museum.

The Museums Association defines a museum as 'an institution which collects, documents, preserves, exhibits and interprets material evidence and associated material for public benefit'. Collections are fundamental to the existence of a museum or gallery. They should not be relegated to the storeroom because they make interpretation difficult. The collections are evidence and their tangible presence helps to validate the story being told. The fact that collections may make the story more complex, difficult to follow, and perhaps contradictory in places is no reason to reject the objects. The skill of the curator lies in the ability to guide the display team to use the collections meaningfully, providing supporting text, graphics, models, hands-on units, and working with demonstrator staff.

The possibilities for interpreting collections are endless. Items can be displayed mutely for their sculptural and aesthetic qualities, they can be examined for their intrinsic significance, or they can be used to illustrate some theme or concept. There is a tendency to group, collect, and interpret objects according to subject area. This approach is often a reflection of the knowledge, skills, and attitudes of the curators rather than intrinsic to the objects themselves. The total separation which often exists between the arts and the sciences is both artificial and unnecessary.

The nature of the prime material will, however, restrict the nature of the display. The aesthetics of art displays suggest that Victorian paintings are best displayed in richly decorated settings while modern works are better seen in bare rooms with painted walls. Neither technique encourages lengthy labelling or the use of distracting elements such as video displays, handsets carrying commentaries, or hands-on experiments. Special rooms or areas may need to be set aside for more complex interpretation of the science in art.

History displays use the technique familiar in most science museums. Large and incomprehensible pieces of equipment are described by long and incomprehensible labels. This traditional technique is now being supplemented by new approaches such as the use of 'role players' who encourage visitors to empathise with those who used similar objects in the past. In many museums this part is played by crafts demonstrators. History museum displays are thus broadly similar to traditional science museum displays and respond in a similar way to scientific interpretation.

Virtually any museum or art gallery collection can therefore be used as a vehicle for increasing the public understanding of science. The beauty of this approach is that it does not require any initial scientific interest or inclination on the part of the visitor. It also fits in well with the cross-curricular emphasis of the national curriculum. A primary school teacher with very limited training in science (an all too common situation) can usually deal effectively with small chunks of science if linked to the subject they know better.

The role of the scientist

Many staff in museums have a very strong sense of territory. This is a useful trait when the collection requires care and security. It is an understandable trait when the work of years is being questioned. However, it also tends to frustrate change when it is needed.

The role of the scientist is likely to be within a triangle of interests. The curatorial staff will be concerned for the physical well-being of their collections and the airing of their academic disciplines. The educational staff will be inclined to guard their relationships with curators and their professional role as trained teachers. Scientists may be concerned with reflecting their academic disciplines accurately within exhibitions.

One difficulty which may arise is in the scientist's lack of awareness of public ignorance. Someone trained in an environment of like-minded people may be surprised at the complete absence of knowledge of the museum visitor in the subject areas that the scientist holds dear. The scientist's role is therefore likely to be concentrated in two areas. The first is the recognition and definition of the scientific links of quite commonplace things. The second is in checking that the greatly simplified interpretation built upon the curators' and educators' experience of their public is not misleading or simply wrong.

A (fictitious) example may help to illustrate the relationship. Responsibility for a local history collection including a fire engine lies in the care of a 'historian/curator'. An education officer is keen to exploit this attractive item as a focus for school and public interest. The key requirement for a working fire engine is the ability to pump water to the top of a high building. This presents a fascinating opportunity for dealing with head pressure. Neither the curator nor the educator has the time or the expertise to represent simply and accurately the fundamental relationships which exist between head pressure, hose diameter, and flow rate. The scientist chosen has that knowledge and is able to provide assurance that any description developed is technically correct. He or she also ensures that similar opportunities to teach about the conversion of kinetic and potential energy are seen and reflected in the display if space permits.

The scientist can have an important continuing relationship where demonstrators, role players or actors are involved in helping to interpret a display with scientific and technical elements. The initial work may be satisfactory and convey accurately the science in the art or history display. The initial training of the interpretive staff may also be satisfactory. However, as time goes by and staff forget, become stale, or leave, the original message can become garbled. There is a need for continuing quality control and training which is best provided on the technical side by someone with a good grasp of science and technology within the display team.

Some practical examples

The first example relates to the Liverpool Museum *Decorative Art* collection of European clocks and watches. The material, it is true, was originally intended to be functional but was interpreted on the gallery mainly in terms of its decorative and stylistic features and ornamentation. In a number of instances the works of the clocks and watches were shown and named but this was a far cry from trying to interpret the history and scientific development of time measurement.

My colleague Peter Reed developed a programme based on this display in 1975 when he was newly appointed as Education Officer for science. He noted how time had always been important to humankind, that it had been measured in various ways: by sundials and nocturnals; the flow of water or sand through a small opening; or the regular burning of an oil lamp or candle. However, it was thousands of years before it was realised that greater accuracy was produced by regular mechanical motions and this led in due course to scientific timekeepers and to the detailed study of the properties of thermal expansion of metals, the mathematical description of a swinging pendulum, the effects of friction and air damping.

The programme led naturally enough through combustion, water flow, and the pendulum, to the quartz crystal and caesium atomic clocks of the twentieth century. The main problem with the programme was that it involved a split session, part of it on the galleries, part of it in a classroom behind the scenes. This was due to the space constraints on the gallery. As such it was difficult

and expensive to operate. It illustrates the need to consider this kind of interpretation during gallery design.

A much more recent example of scientific interpretation of a non-science collection is to be found in the arts/science alliance at the Dulwich Picture Gallery.[7] Here the Education Officer Gillian Wolfe and artist and painting conservator Philippa Abrahams have operated regular cross-curricular sessions for primary school children over the last two years. A brief introductory tour of the gallery focuses on four paintings which use a variety of different colours. This leads naturally to a discussion of different natural and synthetic pigments, the media which are used to bind them, and the supports and grounds which are used to provide the stable surface for the paint. The session describes how the organic and mineral substances are treated to make different colours and the students are allowed to grind and mix them. It is emphasised that many of these processes are not new. They used to be part of the everyday knowledge and work of artists in former times.

The beauty of the session is that it is held on the gallery surrounded by the paintings. The children are able to see and to handle the materials from which the paintings are made in a way that relates to their experience of the world around them. After such a session the experience of seeing a picture or even the painted wall of a room could hardly be the same again. In the space of an hour the children become part of a technological and scientific tradition that stretches back for thousands of years. It is all done without a formula or an equation in sight!

Methods of interpretation

Interpretation can be at a number of levels. The simple label and diagram suffices in many cases. A short video film can animate the explanation. A member of staff or a volunteer demonstrator can adapt the description to reflect the interests of the visitor, while a small bay of hands-on experiments might give insights to the processes and methods of science as well as the explanation.

There is enormous scope for making links and strengthening the relationships between the arts and the sciences. One particular scientist gives a demonstration talk using music as a vehicle for introducing science, particularly at primary school level. He also aims to demystify the subject and to demolish the myth that science is always 'right' rather than a series of approximations attempting to answer pertinent questions. The difficulty faced by museums is how to communicate the uncertainties of science without giving the impression that the results are too unsure or trivial to be worth considering. In a public lecture, a demonstration or a drama performance, the process of approximation, of getting a 'wrong' answer, and of explaining why it was wrong, is a well tried and successful technique. However, the same message displayed mutely on the gallery can create a confused and unconvincing impression. In this case it is often best to provide the visitor with something to do so that they can find out for themselves.

Here also, the techniques are well tried and tested at Launch Pad, the Exploratory, Techniquest, and our own Technology Testbed in Liverpool. Children take to these hands-on activities spontaneously. Adults normally require more encouragement. However, here again we have experienced some weaknesses in the method because most experiments allow for some ambiguity which is inevitably picked up in the visitors' response. This kind of ambiguity can lead to visitor frustration and disappointment if there is no recourse to a demonstrator. The ultimate solution to this kind of problem is better scientific input, better design, and a grouping of related experiments which give a consistent and sustainable result without losing the sense of discovery.

It is wise not to describe displays in a non-scientific context as science. This reflects the cultural attitude of the proportion of the population which feels that science is not for them. It is important that the scientific content emerges naturally from the objects on display and that enthusiasm for the simplicity and interest of the information dispels the worries that might otherwise be felt about something overtly scientific. The idea is to make people aware of scientific ideas without mentioning the term 'science'. It may even be to persuade visitors to do scientific experiments without being made aware that they are in the domain of science. In time they may become accustomed to some of the strengths of science in posing questions and testing outcomes. They may also get to know some of the fictions of science: 'weightless objects', 'frictionless pulleys', and 'perfect gases'. The limitations of simple theories when faced with complex reality should be readily

admitted. The theory of musical instruments provides a fine example of the kind of difficulty to be faced.

The 'science by stealth' approach already occurs to a large extent in our primary school programme. Almost every session in the museum covers science in a cross-curricular sense as part of a lattice of topics. Science is frequently introduced where it will help in the understanding of the object itself, how it worked or was used, or its position in human technological development. For example, our nineteenth-century steam locomotive from the Liverpool and Manchester railway was part of a social revolution of personal mobility. It is explained that it burns coal (which very few primary school children have ever seen); the burning coal generates hot gas; the hot gas turns water to steam; the steam is contained at high pressure like the steam in a pressure cooker; and the steam forces the pistons to and fro. In another area the session on the Greeks looks at the designs and pictures on Greek pottery. The pictures themselves tell a lot about the appearance, dress, and activities of the people while the colouring of the red pottery ground and the black decorative designs are explained in terms of the different degrees of oxidation of different clays in the fierce heat of the furnace.

It can be seen that all objects are being approached from three directions: the aesthetics of appearance and decoration; the role of the object in society and the use that people made of it; and the science and technology available to sustain the society and to make possible the human and aesthetic outcomes.

What then should be the role of the scientist in this scheme of museum interpretation? In most respects many of my museum education colleagues seem content as they are. They specialise mainly in non-scientific subjects. They glean the basic science that they think they need and they impart it in a way that they can understand. They know that there is much that they do not understand and they make it clear to class teachers and to school children that there is more to be found out if they are interested.

I must confess to some unease about this state of affairs. I know that education staff are well trained in filtering, absorbing, and communicating knowledge. They undoubtedly do a good job. I also know that there are many scientists who are extremely poor communicators and who would confuse, upset, and alienate their audiences and destroy the very enthusiasm and interest the museum is seeking to create. However, I know from experience both in the Planetarium and in Technology Testbed that lack of knowledge means that opportunities are missed and the message can get garbled.

The right scientific input at the right time well supported by educational and curatorial expertise could achieve a transformation in the interpretation of our huge and diverse collections of art and humanities. That input needs to be at the stage when new displays and interpretive programmes are being developed; when they are first implemented; and on a continuing basis to provide quality control and retraining.

I believe there is scope the other way round as well. All too few people appreciate the rugged simplicity of a cast iron beam engine, the exquisite perfection of a large telescope mirror, or understand the lives and motivations of the people who make and use them. Still less do they understand the classic simplicity of a mathematical equation. Perhaps the time has come to emphasise the aesthetics and humanity of science as a further stage in our quest for public understanding and awareness.

The future

The steps required to promote the public understanding of science through non-science museums are: technical and scientific advice; the funding of initial costs; volunteer organisation and training; maintenance, quality control, and retraining; and, above all, a commitment at senior level to reflecting the scientific elements of the collections as a normal part of museum and gallery practice.

Museums have a problem recruiting trained and competent scientific staff. For many small museums there will be no scientists on the staff and no means of assessing the scientific potential of the collections. They require access to scientific knowledge through consultancies, education advisers, polytechnics, and universities.

Over half of the costs incurred by museums and galleries are spent on keeping their buildings open to the public. This involves maintaining fire and security systems, providing competent warding staff, cleaning and renewing the display areas, and operating admission points, shops, and cafés. Such expenditure continues regardless of the nature of

the display. Additional sections and units inserted in the displays to exploit their potential for public awareness of science will carry relatively small overheads.

Perhaps the most challenging aspect of the programme is the need to involve people in a voluntary capacity. Demographic changes may help to achieve this. Over the next 10 years, the number of retired people is expected to increase substantially as a result of a small increase in the number of people over 60 and a significant increase in the number taking early retirement at age 55. This is seen as part of a general trend towards a '35: 35: 35' working life in which a substantial proportion of the population works 35 hours a week, 35 weeks a year, for 35 years of their life.

This trend is set to continue through the early years of the twenty-first century until by 2025 nearly one in three of the population will be in the over-55 age group compared with one in four at present. This over-55 age group will contain a greater proportion of women with formal education, occupational retirement pensions, and disposable income than was the case in former generations.

However, we must not be too euphoric about the future. We know that barring some miraculous change we may also have followed some American examples.[8] It is suggested that before too long 85 per cent of children in the US will be in one-parent homes, 25 per cent of the population will be illiterate, and 2 per cent homeless. The average citizen will also have watched 16,000 hours of television by the age of 20.

The affluent, ageing population, and the younger, less stable, less literate, television-watching population need to be brought together in our museums to share the enjoyment of understanding our scientific culture. Examples are already available. The Friends organisations on Merseyside provide tremendous help in ship maintenance and guiding services and have recently been involved in a Discovery Centre project helping parents and children to enjoy a small archaeology interactive display. However, little has been done in science and technology. Volunteer training programmes for those in their 'sunset' years would seem to be a useful first step in any general programme to bring animated and affordable science to general museums.

The role of the science specialist in these training courses could be considerable and, as discussed previously, the continuing need for maintenance, quality control, and retraining also requires scientific input. That continuing relationship is an essential part of making science and technology interpretation a routine part of museum and art gallery practice.

The limit of expectations

Jerry Wellington in *Sharing Science* described the growth of understanding very simply and elegantly in terms of knowledge THAT, knowledge HOW, and knowledge WHY. Most adults know that milk in the sun goes 'off'. Very few know how or why.[9] Progress from knowledge to understanding requires curiosity – a desire to know how and why – and an explanation. In most cases, how and why are not directly observable and can only be inferred or demonstrated by analogues.

The question posed by this paper is: how far is it possible to adapt the museum visitors' experience to develop knowledge and awareness of THAT, HOW, and WHY, to make the experience enjoyable and to create a perception of science as something that is basically simple and relevant to everyday life, to history, to art, and to the future?

Part of the answer is in the new national curriculum which provides targets for knowledge and understanding that students should achieve as they move through the different levels of schooling. The aim is presumably that all adults in the future should share a common level of knowledge corresponding roughly to the national curriculum.

It is, of course, perfectly possible for any museum with sufficient space and money to create the 160-odd experimental bays to illustrate or demonstrate every level of every attainment target of the science curriculum (as it was). Such a package would be fairly costly to make and maintain but would be perfectly within the scope of the work of a normal museum or science centre. However, this could rapidly be followed by 137 bays for mathematics and 50 bays for technology. Unfortunately, such displays, in isolation, might simply reinforce the alienation of science from everyday life.

However, the aim of school science teaching is to motivate and enable a proportion of children, at a later date, to become scientists. Hence the basic skills of the scientist form part of the curriculum. For adults visiting a museum or gallery the position is rather different. They have already made their career decisions and most of them have decided not to be scientists.

The aim proposed for the museum or gallery is thus mainly to inform the visitor of the scientific content and background of the objects on display without the visitor necessarily realising that science is involved. The interpretation need not attempt to explain the scientific processes, which would, in many cases, involve language and concepts that the visitor would not understand. However, scientific input to the writing of clear, simple labels, the training of volunteer demonstrators and guides, and the design of a selection of hands-on experiments are essential elements in communicating the latent science in our museums to 70 million visitors each year. For the present it may be sufficient to increase awareness; in the longer term understanding may follow.

Table 1: science processes at primary school level

1 The use of graphical and symbolic representation
2 The use of apparatus and measuring instruments
3 Observation
4 The interpretation and application of information and concepts
5 The planning of investigations
6 The performance of investigations

The choice of appropriate processes when planning an investigation and presenting results indicated that the processes were being used in the right context.

Table 2: science concepts at primary school level

1 Interaction of living things with their environment
2 Living things and their life processes
3 Forces
4 Energy
5 Classification and structure of matter
6 Chemical interactions

The interpretation of presented information with reasons related to appropriate concept indicated that concepts were being understood and deployed.

Table 3: attitudes to science at primary school level

Participation at school or at home in, for example:

1 Problem solving
2 Watching TV science programme
3 Reading science book
4 Watching science demonstration
5 Looking after animal
6 Weighing out ingredients for cooking, etc.

Children were asked if they had participated in an activity and if they wished to do more. The degree to which children wished to do more of an activity was indicative of their attitude towards that activity.

Notes and references

1 *Museums: Generators of Culture*, report of the 15th General Conference of the International Council of Museums (The Hague: the ICOM '89 Foundation, 1991)

2 Feist, A, and Eckstein, J (eds), *Cultural Trends Issue 8: 1990* (London: Policy Studies Institute, 1991)
Middleton, V, *New Visions for Independent Museums in the UK*, (Chichester: Association of Independent Museums, 1990)

3 *The Road to Wigan Pier? Managing Local Authority Museums and Art Galleries* (London: HMSO, 1991)
Museums and Galleries Commission: The National Museums (London: HMSO, 1988)
Museums and Galleries Commission: Local Authorities and Museums (London: HMSO, 1991)

4 Porter, G, in the introduction to *Sharing Science* (London: The Nuffield Foundation, 1989)

5 *Science in the National Curriculum* (London: HMSO for the Department of Education and Science and the Welsh Office, 1989)

6 Russell, T (ed), *Science at Age 11* (London: HMSO for the Assessment of Performance Unit, 1988)

7 Channon, A, 'The art/science alliance at the Dulwich Picture Gallery', in *Art and Schools* (London: HMSO for the Department of Education and Science and the Office of Arts and Libraries, 1990)

8 *Museums: Generators of Culture*

9 Wellington, J, 'Attitudes before understanding: the contribution of interactive centres to science education', in *Sharing Science*, p31

'Wonders in one closet shut': the educational potential of history of science museums

Willem Hackmann

In February 1683, Robert Plot, author of *The Natural History of Oxfordshire* (1677), alchemist, chemist, and antiquarian, arrived in London to assist Elias Ashmole with crating up his extensive collection of 'natural curiosities' and 'rarities'. This typical seventeenth-century collection had originally belonged to the Tradescants, father and son, and the manner in which it passed on to Ashmole is still a matter of controversy for those who worry about such things. For a decade delighted visitors could visit Tradescant's Ark at Ashmole's house in Lambeth before it moved on to Oxford to the Ashmolean Museum. The collection was shipped in 26 large packing cases, loaded onto barges, and then into 12 carts, which arrived at the newly built Museum at Oxford on 20 March 1683, for the formal opening two months later by James Duke of York, the brother of Charles II, and the future James II. Royal patronage had been confidently expected, for Charles' Royal Arms and monogram were placed above the North entrance of the Museum, but was never forthcoming. Charles was also the patron of those two other English seventeenth-century scientific institutions, the Royal Society and the Royal Observatory.

The common perception of the history of science museums in this country has been distorted because the present usurper of the famous Ashmolean name is justly celebrated for its collections in art and archaeology. The original Ashmolean, the first public museum in this country, was not an arts museum at all, but celebrated the new scientific outlook of the Renaissance. It was intended for 'the knowledge of Nature' acquired through 'the inspection of Particulars'. In it were assembled specimens from all creation, as in Noah's Ark; a metaphor enshrined even in the architecture, for the tall, slightly ungainly, building has all the appearance of Noah's Ark floating down Broad Street. In modern terms it was the first of the science centres: its three floors comprised the Museum (top floor), the School of Natural History (lecture gallery on the ground floor), and the Chemical Laboratory (basement). As such it is the product of the scientific revolution that was spreading across the educated world. Until about 1860 all the known sciences were taught there, and the modern science departments of the University have their origins in the Museum.[1]

Richard Gregory has pointed out that providing public understanding of science and technology through hands-on science is not a new idea, but that it is clearly expressed by Francis Bacon in his *New Atlantis* (1626).[2] Bacon describes how the technology and science of his day could be made available in his imaginary Salomon's House, a place for all to visit and so enter the drama of seeking truth through science and share the harvesting of its benefits. Science was seen as a social activity in which contributions were made according to individual abilities and personal interests. This was the role of the Royal Society (established in 1660), and the original Ashmolean was also such a Salomon's House. In it the methods of collecting antiquities were applied to the natural world. This collecting also extended to natural phenomena as observed using the new tools of the scientific revolution: the telescope and microscope, followed by the air pump and electrical machine. These novel instrument-induced observations could not be contained in exhibition cases, but could be collected, described, and catalogued in books which could then be housed in the Museum. Thus, Bacon voiced the commonly held opinion that the study of the book of nature – of God's creations in all its guises, from tattooed skin of Eskimo, to the dodo (of which the Ashmolean had one of the few examples), from microscope observations of the compound eye of the fly, to the observation of light through a prism – led both to a deeper understanding of the Creator and to material benefits.

With the establishment of the Museum of the History of Science in this fine Renaissance building in 1924 history turned full circle.[3] In many respects similar forces had come into play as those apparent in the original foundations, and the new museum was the result of the increasing interest in historical scientific artefacts – a kind of archaeology of science to mirror the archaeology of past civilisations. In both instances there were a few enthusiasts who, by applying the right political pressures, managed to get their respective museums off the ground. The Noah's Ark metaphor was also continued by the new founding Curator, Robert T Gunther, who regarded the new institution as an act of faith in hostile times to salvage the records of a past that was disappearing as science was developing ever more quickly.[4]

The Science Museum in London has quite a different origin. It goes back to the opening, in 1857, of the South Kensington Museum, which was an offshoot of the Department of Science and Art formed in 1853 under the Board of Trade. The Department was the result of a proposal by the Commissioners for the Great Exhibition of 1851 that the profits of this Exhibition should be devoted to fund an institution which should 'serve to increase the means of Industrial Education and extend the influence of Science and Art upon Productive Industry'.[5] The Great Exhibition showed that Britain was falling behind in science-based industries and this led to the reform of science education in schools and universities, and to the founding of the Science Museum to educate the emerging class of science technicians. Thus, we have (at least) two groups of modern 'science museums' with quite distinctive origins and intentions. This has to be recognised in order to understand how these institutions see their present roles.

The first group of museums have come from the history of science and the second from science education. The former include the History of Science Museum in Oxford, the Whipple Museum in Cambridge, the Museum of the History of Science in Florence, the University Museum in Utrecht, the Museum Boerhaave in Leyden, and Teylers Museum in Haarlem, Holland. The latter include the Science Museum in London and the Deutsches Museum in Munich. The former museums have concentrated on the historical study of scientific artefacts in all its facets (antiquarian connoisseurship, the development of small-scale precision technology, the structure of the instrument-making trade, and scientific questions such as the relationsip of instruments to experiments and the development of scientific concepts); the latter institutions on using these instruments as an aid to teaching modern science and technology.

The relationship between the traditional history of science museums and the history of science was, in the past, somewhat schizophrenic, to say the least. Historians of science, used to handling documents, tended to see scientific instruments as 'gadgets', and H T Pledge's aphorism, 'the love of gadgets is only the beginning of wisdom', was common currency.[6] Apart from a few areas in which it was impossible to ignore the artefacts, such as in the history of astronomy, there was little communication between historians of scientific instruments and historians of science. Even today it is possible to do a course in Oxford on the seventeenth-century scientific movement without ever having looked through a Hooke or Culpeper microscope, or seen a Hauksbee air pump. To interject a personal note, I began my own odyssey in the history of experimental instruments 20-odd years ago when I discovered to my astonishment that historians were writing about eighteenth-century experimental science without ever having seen the apparatus that formed the basis of this work. In recent years an interest in the methodology and sociology of experimentation has led to a greater awareness of the importance of the experimental apparatus.[7]

According to Richard Gregory, remarkably little science is found in the traditional museums of science. He asks whether it is simply that science museums seldom attempt explanations because explaining is not their traditional aim, or whether the concepts and principles underlying appearances are just too hard to present without the kind of background knowledge instilled over the years in schools and universities.[8] The question is an important one, but first of all a distinction should be made between the roles of science museums and history of science museums. Traditionally, history of science museums have tended to have static displays concentrating on the diversity and evolution of specific devices placed in a historical context, while science museums have made more use of moving models to illustrate scientific concepts or technological processes. History is used, but only as a didactic tool to explain how the modern processes have been arrived at. An important impetus propelling the movement of the interactive science centres has undoubtedly been a dissatisfaction with the traditional museum displays, and the belief not only that 'science is fun' (or at least that it can be made to be seen to be fun), but that it can be better taught through interactive demonstrations and experiments. Richard Gregory suggests that besides these 'exploratories' there should perhaps also be 'explanatories' with different kinds of displays for exploring the abstract concepts underlying much of present day science.

Reference has already been made to Bacon's hypothetical House of Salomon in which he kept engines, instruments for measuring, and all the sciences and technology of his time. What is described here is the way in which science (or experimental philosophy as it was then called) began to be taught at universities in the late seventeenth century at the original Ashmolean and elsewhere. Thus, interactive or hands-on science is not all that new - apart from its name. Science also became a popular form of entertainment performed by travelling lecturers who enlivened their shows with special (sometimes spectacular) machines which demonstrated scientific principles: electrical machines, model cranes or pile drivers, air pumps, and many others. These demonstrations, apart from showing the latest scientific discoveries such as the prismatic colours of white light, also illustrated the potential of the latest science-based technologies, such as blowing up model ships with underwater mines filled with gunpowder or protecting model houses filled with gunpowder by miniature lightning conductors. The same machines and didactic experiments formed the basis of the university experimental physics courses described in formal (highly experimental) textbooks from the 1720s. Thus, science was mainly taught by means of didactic demonstrations, and this has continued in some respects until today in the school and university curriculum.

The first children's book on popular science was published in 1761, advertised as a 'philosophy of tops and balls'; the final edition appeared in 1838.[9] The nineteenth century was the golden age for public scientific demonstrations, and for scientific entertainment in the home. Apart from books to whet the appetite such as David Brewster's *Letters on Natural Magic* (1833), there were also many scientific toys: mathematical puzzles, Cartesian divers, anamorphic pictures, model boats powered by camphor pellets, zoetropes and phenakistoscopes, balancing tricks with coins and tumblers, and optical illusions such as Pepper's ghost.[10] Perhaps this has been killed off by the more passive entertainment first of the radio and then the television. The general public may also have become more hopeless about ever being able to understand science because of the tremendous growth in scientific knowledge and the breakdown of classical physics. It could be argued that the recent interactive science centre movement has

taken the place of the earlier home-based recreational science.

The problem as seen from an historian's perspective is that modern science teaching and the interactive science movement is conducted mostly outside any historical framework, and this is where history of science museums could be helpful with their vast stock of historical material. That history could be a useful element in the teaching of modern physics was recognised by several twentieth-century physics textbook writers, although most of their colleagues probably thought this approach somewhat eccentric.[11] More recently, the value of this approach has been recognised by science teachers, and not only have there been at least two conferences in the 1980s on using the history of physics in physics education, several museums and university physics departments have developed facsimile historical experiments for modern physics courses.[12] An exciting new development is the use of interactive multimedia computer systems to enable students to perform historical experiments on the computer in real time.

Historical instruments have been used in science teaching in various ways. Firstly, the study of the development of their capabilities has allowed the production of 'technological frontier' graphs which demonstrate what was technically feasible at a particular time, such as the accuracy of the chemical balance or the resolution of microscope objectives. If scientific discoveries were not keeping pace with the instrument's increased capabilities this could be because of conceptual blocks. Such discussions illustrate to the student the importance of the contemporary theoretical framework, painstaking observations, and background experience.

Repeating actual experiments can give the student insight into the problems faced when they were first performed. William Gilbert's theory of electrical attraction in 1600, as indicated by his 'versorium', might have been substantially modified if he had placed his simple electrical indicator on a drinking glass or a non-conducting table cloth. Replicating his experiments with a nineteenth-century copy at Oxford demonstrated how difficult it must have been for him to interpret the ambiguous movements of the needle. In another replication experiment, B S Finn of the Smithsonian (now the National Museum of American History) gained insight into the efficiency of Desaguliers' air pump of 1742, which allowed him to produce an electrostatic glow but no electrical attraction. Finn demonstrated that this only occurred at rather low pressures showing that Desaguliers' air pump was very good for the time. However, if his pump had been even better, he would have discovered to his astonishment that both the electrical attraction and the glow would have vanished, and this may well have caused a significant change to his working hypothesis concerning the properties of electricity. Many other important historical experiments can be replicated in this way, either with actual apparatus or using multimedia interactive computer systems. Apart from anything else, it will demonstrate to the student that the process of 'seeing', even in science, is a complex affair.

Science museums, history of science museums, and interactive science centres all have their part to play in the public understanding of science. The history of science museums, through their collections and also through their origins, are the most grounded in the past and this can be used to advantage. They should assume the role of

Richard Gregory's explanatories, by means of lectures, thoughtful static exhibitions, replication experiments, and interactive computer displays to demonstrate the function of the historical apparatus.[13] What seems to be lacking in the interactive science centres is a sense of history which can often be an important aid to understanding modern science.[14] History can lead to the appreciation that the present day scientific edifice was constructed (often laboriously) brick by brick; this might make the public's attempt to understand science appear more manageable and less dispiriting. It might make the public appreciate Newton's sense of wonder when he wrote at the end of his life about his scientific endeavours:

> I do not know what I may appear to the world; but to myself I seem only like a boy, playing on the seashore, and diverting myself in now and then finding a smooth pebble or a prettier shell than ordinary, whilst the great ocean of truth lay undiscovered before me.[15]

Notes and references

1 Turner, A, 'A world of wonders in one closet shut', *History of Science*, 24 (1986), pp209-15
Simcock, A, *The Ashmolean Museum and Oxford Science 1683-1983* (Oxford: Museum of the History of Science, 1984)
Simcock, A, 'An ark for the history of science', *Iatul Quarterly*, 1 (1987), pp196-215

2 Gregory, R, 'Turning minds on to science by hands-on exploration: the nature and potential of the hands-on medium', *Sharing Science* (London: Nuffield Foundation, 1989), pp1-9

3 From 1924-1935 the Museum was called the Lewis Evans Collection.

4 Simcock, A (ed), *Robert T Gunther and the Old Ashmolean* (Oxford: Museum of the History of Science, 1985)
Gunther, A, *Robert T Gunther: a Pioneer in the History of Science* (Oxford: Printed for the Subscribers, 1967) *Early Science in Oxford*, vol. 15

5 Follett, D, *The Rise of the Science Museum under Sir Henry Lyons* (London: Science Museum, 1978), pp1-9
Second Report of the Commissioners for the 1851 Exhibition (London: Commissioners for the 1851 Exhibition, 1852), p11

6 Pledge, H, 'Prefatory note 1939-1959', *Science since 1500*, (London: HMSO, 2nd ed, 1966), p3

7 The different approaches are discussed in Hackmann, W, 'Instrumentation in the theory and practice of science: scientific instruments as evidence and as an aid to discovery', *Annali dell' Istituto e Museo di Storia della Scienza*, 10 (1985), pp87-115, and in Hackmann, W, 'Scientific instruments: models of brass and aids to discovery', in Gooding, D, Pinch, T, and Schaffer, S (eds), *The Uses of Experiments* (Cambridge: Cambridge University Press, 1989), pp31-65. For an interesting discussion on Faraday in these terms, see Gooding, D, *Experiment and the Making of Meaning* (London: Kluwer Academic, 1990), and concerning modern physics, Galison, P, *How Experiments End* (Chicago: University of Chicago Press, 1987).

8 Gregory, R, p7

9 Tom Telescope, *The Newtonian System of Philosophy adapted to the Capacities of Young Gentlemen and Ladies* (London, 1761)

10 Turner, G, 'Recreational science', chapter 16 in *Nineteenth-Century Scientific Instruments* (London: Sotheby Publications, 1983)

11 Taylor, L, *Physics The Pioneer Science*, 2 vols (New York: Dover, 1941)
Shamos, M, *Great Experiments in Physics* (New

York: Holt, Rhinehart and Winston, 1964)

12 Bevilacqua, F, and Kennedy, P (eds), *Using History of Physics in Innovatory Physics Education* (Pavia: International Commission on Physics Education and Centro Studi per la Didadittica della Facoltà di Scienze Matematiche, Fisiche e Naturali of Pavia University, 1983); Thomsen, P (ed), *Science Education and the History of Physics* (Aarhus: Centre for Studies in Physics Education, Aarhus University, 1986). Such experiments have been developed by Jürgen Teichmann at the Deutsches Museum, at the Physics Department of the University of Oldenburg under the rubric 'From the electrical machine to the theory of ether', and at the Bakken Library and Museum of Electricity in Life, Minneapolis, among others. The Bakken team have developed a simple kit for secondary schools, marketed with a video and booklet.

13 The educational aspects were never thought through by the enthusiasts who founded these museums, nor are most of them at present given the resources to make such a policy feasible. The British Association has been involved in the public understanding of science ever since the 1830s which surely demonstrates the difficulty of this task.

14 I have tried to follow this approach in my *Scientific Amusement Arcade. An Exhibition Commemorating the 150th Meeting of the British Association for the Advancement of Science at Oxford* (Oxford, 1988).

15 Westfall, R, *Never at Rest: A Biography of Sir Isaac Newton* (Cambridge: Cambridge University Press, 1987), p863, footnote 296

Building positive attitudes to science: new ideas from museums and other groups

Peter Briggs

Promoting the public understanding of science and technology is, explicitly or implicitly, the purpose of nearly all museums of science, industry and engineering. For the most part they try to achieve this through collecting and displaying objects and through mounting exhibitions. But increasingly museums are also getting involved in other activities which seek to improve the public's awareness and understanding of science and technology. Some of these additional activities also make use of their object collections and exhibitions; others do not really depend on them at all. This paper describes a few activities through which museums are promoting public understanding on a broader canvas and discusses some of the issues which they raise. It is written from a UK perspective although the activities used as examples are drawn from a number of countries. Likewise it is written from outside the museum world rather than from within it.

In the US the Boston Museum of Science started to set up public outreach programmes about 30 years ago. In 1988 it launched a new programme which it dubbed *Science-by-mail*.[1] An imaginative and popular scheme, the number of its participants has nearly trebled in three years. *Science-by-mail* now involves over 20,000 young people and 2,300 scientists.

Young people in school grades four to nine (usually aged nine to fourteen) sign up for *Science-by-mail* either as individuals or in groups of up to four. They are sent a science challenge package three times a year in December, February, and April, and are also put into contact with a professional scientist who has agreed to act as a 'pen-pal' to them. The packages, which are put together by a team of scientists and teachers, contain a science-based challenge or problem for the young people to tackle and a variety of materials which enable them to explore the problem and to conduct investigations testing out ideas. Typical problems used in the scheme since it started in 1988 include, 'invent a new way of keeping time', or 'devise a way of disposing of rubbish on a space voyage'. The challenges

encourage children to explore the scientific principles lying behind everyday experience such as magic tricks or the decomposition of bananas.

The scheme is extremely flexible. Participants work on their own or as part of a group. Some register through their school and tackle the problem in either class time or as part of a science club activity; some join through a youth club or other youth organisation; and others register as individuals or family groups. In working on the problem, the young people can consult their teachers, parents or anyone else, including their scientist pen-pal. Their solution, which has to be in writing, on tape or in another form suitable for posting, is then sent to their scientist pen-pal who reviews it and writes back with comments and suggestions on the young people's ideas and the approach they have adopted. There are no right or wrong answers, no passes or failures, no winners or losers. Whatever their age or ability, whatever amount of time the young people have invested in exploring the problem, their scientist pen-pal writes back with notes of encouragement, guidance and support.

Camp-in is another activity which has grown to be a common feature of the programmes offered by museums and science centres throughout North America but which is less common in Europe. Groups of young people from schools, youth organisations such as the scouts and guides, or those taking part in educational holidays arrive at the museum in the early evening with sleeping bags and other overnight gear. When they depart after breakfast the next day, they will have spent the night taking part in a series of exciting activities which will typically include workshops, film shows, quizzes, competitions and treasure hunts as well as some time to eat and sleep. They may have worked on topics related to school projects or undertaken badge activities for their youth group. Resources for *Camp-in* include the staff and exhibits of the host museum or science centre and, in addition, the campers' own group leaders or teachers. Pre-*Camp-in* briefing sessions are commonly held for the leaders of participating groups to enable them to learn how to cope with the logistics of the overnight arrangements and how to use the museum's resources to best advantage. The numbers involved in such events vary widely. *Camp-in* at Science North in Ontario, for example, caters for 100 people per night whereas anything up to 1,000 young people might be involved in a *Camp-in* at the Franklin Institute in Philadelphia.

Why are these sort of schemes of particular interest? The Royal Society's 1985 report on the public understanding of science acknowledged that the process of building long-term positive attitudes to science and technology has to start with young people.[2] Irrespective of their future role in life, all young people should be able to grow up confidently in a scientific and technological age. They need to recognise the ways in which science and technology impinge on their lives and appreciate the contribution they make to personal and social well-being. But there is another, more specific need. To maintain any country's research base and to enable its industry to keep up to date in a highly competitive world, an adequate supply of people with specialist scientific and technical skills is essential. So, in addition to being made generally aware, many young people have to be motivated to study scientific and technological subjects and to be attracted into careers which make use of them.

Motivating young people is something that museums, especially those which encourage a hands-on approach, appear to do particularly well anyway. But *Camp-in* has the added benefit of bringing together a large group of people, sometimes as we have seen as many as 1,000 per night. There is something especially attractive for young people about being part of an activity which involves large numbers of people. Confirmation of this comes from the experience of the British Association Youth Section (BAYS). For the past ten years it has organised an annual activity day for young people, their parents and teachers at London's scientific museums or London Zoo. These BAYSDAYs, as they are called, have been extremely popular, each attracting up to 5,000 people. The formula is simple. BAYS organises a programme of talks, presentations, exhibitions, problem-solving challenges, competitions and other activities. The museums provide a spacious and attractive venue. Their own regular attractions ensure that the participants are never short of things to occupy them during the day. The success of BAYSDAYs is undoubtedly due to the appeal

of a large event as well as the attraction of the programme of participative activities. Equally successful BAYSDAYs are now held at museums and science centres in Manchester, Newcastle, Bristol, and Cardiff, as well as in London.

Camp-in of course also has something else going for it. As many a weary parent will testify there is something especially magical to the young about an all-night activity!

Special *Science-by-mail* days add this large event dimension to the basic *Science-by-mail* scheme. At the culmination of each year's programme the Boston Museum runs a special day of activities in which all young people participating in the scheme in the Boston area get a chance to meet their scientist pen-pals. Similar days are run in other areas where the scheme is in operation. But it is the link that *Science-by-mail* forges between young people and professional scientists that is of most interest.

Opinion surveys in the UK suggest that there is considerable public interest in science and technology but that, paradoxically perhaps, scientists and engineers themselves are not held in particularly high esteem. In 1988, Durant, Evans and Thomas found that over 80 per cent of the British public professed to moderate or high interest in new scientific discoveries, inventions and technologies.[3] Yet, only a year later, a survey carried out by *New Scientist* showed that only 20 per cent of people had great confidence in scientific institutions,[4] and in 1990 a *Daily Telegraph* poll showed scientists to be way down the list of those the public most trusted to tell the truth.[5] Even accepting that such results need to be interpreted with caution, it still seems fairly clear that public understanding programmes need to have more than one objective. Not only do people need to be aware of scientific 'facts', they need to appreciate the nature of scientific enquiry and the provisionality of its results, and they need to recognise that scientists themselves are human beings just like the rest of us.

Scientists and engineers themselves must surely have a key role to play in achieving this latter objective. No group can humanise scientists better than scientists themselves; nobody is better placed to provide positive role models for the aspiring scientists of tomorrow than the real-life scientists of today. This belief is reflected in the frequently repeated call for the introduction of characters with scientific or technical jobs into radio or television soap operas. But the best schemes are likely to be those through which direct links are forged between young people and scientists and engineers.

This is where *Science-by-mail* scores highly. It sets out to change the stereotypical image of the scientist. It certainly succeeded in the case of a 10-year-old Boston girl who told a reporter: 'Before, when I thought of a scientist, I thought of a little old man with whiskers and a white lab coat'. Her pen-pal was a 30-year-old pregnant biochemist!

Apart from some notable exceptions, such as London's Natural History Museum which is a scientific research institute as well as a museum, scientists themselves are not among the objects that most museums collect. So where do those involved in the Boston scheme come from? Most are recruited from professional scientific organisations, in particular the American Association for the Advancement of Science; Sigma XI, the Scientific Research Society; and the Association for Women in Science.

Science-by-mail is a versatile and flexible scheme. It helps to excite young people about science and technology and puts them in touch with scientists and engineers. It can also help teachers, enthuse parents and enable scientists to become more involved in encouraging the young by sharing their experience and expertise.

All this is music to the ears of anyone interested in promoting the public understanding of science. What is not obvious, however, is why *Science-by-mail* is run by a museum. As we have seen already, its major resources – the scientists themselves – are not among the museum's primary assets and have to be recruited from outside. Joan Stanley, the National Program Manager of *Science-by-mail*, points out that in Boston the philosophy of the museum's outreach programmes – offering the public at large an opportunity to become acquainted and involved with science despite their geographical location – is as important as the historically based collection philosophy.

Science-by-mail seems to me to point to both the pitfalls and the opportunities which abound in this field of expanding interest. As recognition of the importance of increasing the public understanding of science grows, so does the number of initiatives designed to promote it and the number of organisations involved in doing so. While it would be wrong for the representative of one such organisation to be too defensive about this, we should ask whether 'letting a thousand flowers bloom' either in terms of activities within organisations or in terms

of organisations themselves is necessarily the strategy most likely to lead to success.

In a not-unrelated area of concern in the UK, that of fostering better education-industry links, the number of organisations running programmes of one sort or another is vast and continues to grow. It leaves many people bewildered, failing to understand the subtle differences between the organisations and their programmes: crystal clear and so important to those on the inside, but almost impossible to discern and entirely insignificant to outsiders. It means that the funds available to support such activities are spread more and more thinly and it results in organisations which on the surface deny that they are in competition having to devote more and more effort to fostering their public image as they, in fact, vie with their so-called non-competitors for the available funds. It is difficult to believe that the overall objective of better education/industry links is furthered by this approach.

There is a real danger that the same pattern will develop in organisations with a stake in promoting the public understanding of science. It would surely be much better for the strengths and distinctive contributions of each to be identified and agreement reached as to who will do what. Much added value could then be generated by co-operative activities.

Science-by-mail is enhanced by, indeed would be difficult without, the links it has forged with professional scientific societies. Examples of co-operative activities which operate to the mutual advantage of both partners can be found in the UK. They include the Science Book Prizes, which are a joint activity of the Science Museum in London and the Committee on the Public Understanding of Science (COPUS). Sponsored by Rhône-Poulenc, two prizes of £10,000 are presented to the authors of the year's best popular science book for general readers and for young people. An imaginative and important initiative, the prizes have benefited greatly from the co-operation that lies behind them, as have the public profiles of their sponsoring organisations. Similarly the BAYSDAYs mentioned earlier are not only extremely effective at motivating and enthusing young people, they also provide clear benefits for both the British Association and the host museums, and foster a sense of co-operation rather then competition between them.

One final lesson of *Science-by-mail* should not be

overlooked. The idea is not wholly original. It came from Dr Innabeth Miller, a Boston Museum employee at the time of its inception. During a visit to Israel she observed a mathematics programme in which students solved problems and mailed their solutions to a mentor who in turn corresponded with them. As with many of the best ideas, Dr Miller translated what she had seen in Israel into a different context with great effect. Those of us who struggle to find effective ways of promoting the public understanding of science should not feel that our only course of action is to wrestle with ideas for completely novel schemes. It is at least as important to observe what works well in other countries and fields and to use our imagination to see the possibilities that might be created by a transformation across national or subject boundaries. In promoting the public understanding of science, a little lateral thinking can go a long way.

Notes and references

1 I am very grateful to Joan Stanley, National Program Manager for *Science-by-mail*, for providing information about the scheme and its success.

2 *The Public Understanding of Science* (London: The Royal Society, 1985)

3 Durant, J R, Evans, G A, and Thomas, G P, 'The public understanding of science', *Nature*, 340 (1989), p11

4 Kenward, M, 'Science stays up the poll', *New Scientist*, 1682 (16 September 1989), p57

5 *Daily Telegraph* (20 August 1990), p10

Travelling exhibitions and the public understanding of science

Norman Tomlin

Museums have been producing travelling exhibitions of all types and sizes for a number of years. It is probably fair to say that most have tended to be art-based, whether fine, applied, historical or contemporary. There are a number of reasons why this has been the case. By comparing the situation in the arts with that in the sciences, and by reviewing past attempts at widely distributed science and technology exhibitions, it will be possible to suggest a strategy to tackle the problem and to promote the public understanding of science.

Comparison with the arts

The popularity of art as a subject for travelling exhibitions can be attributed in the main to a combination of the following factors:

 i   The objects are relatively small and easily transportable.
 ii Suitable venues are available.
 iii Grant-giving bodies exist.
 iv National, subject-related organisations are there for support.
 v   There is an established culture of organising exhibitions.
 vi Limited interpretation is needed leading to less cost and more flexibility in design.
 vii Exhibitions are used as a means of communicating research.

Obviously, promoters of the public understanding of science can only have control over some of these factors.

It is possible to find suitable venues in provincial science museums as well as in other venues such as libraries and leisure centres. It is also possible for science exhibitions to be compact and easily transportable. Exhibitions concerned with science do tend to require a large amount of supporting interpretive material which is costly to research, design and produce. This interpretive material also leads to a relatively limited range of display options, often using a commercial display system which may or may not fit the host venue. The travelling exhibition produced by British Gas, made using a display system comprising coated steel tubes, encountered this problem. The exhibition needed all-round access and both layout and height were fixed. In my own museum there was a headroom margin of less than 10cm and it was extremely difficult to fit the exhibition between the pillars regularly spaced through the museum. I doubt if these problems would occur with many art exhibitions, except perhaps the larger sculpture installations.

All of the difficulties above can be overcome by careful design and are therefore not valid reasons for the lack of travelling exhibitions in science and technology. It is true that there is nothing like as long a tradition of touring exhibitions in science as there is in the arts, but since this factor cannot be influenced it must be disregarded for the purposes of this paper. This leaves a smaller set of differences setting art apart from science and technology: the availability of grant-giving bodies; the existence of national, fund-raising organisations; and the use of exhibitions as a means of communicating research.

In the arts there are a number of bodies such as the Arts Council and the Crafts Council which give both financial and organisational support to travelling exhibitions. In the case of the Arts Council there is an extensive network of regional organisations such as Northern Arts able to fund regional initiatives.

The Crafts Council provides an excellent model of what could be achieved in science and technology. Exhibitions of craft produced by museums, galleries or individuals throughout the UK are made available for loan to other institutions through the Crafts Council. Those setting up new exhibitions send details to the Crafts Council which publishes a list of available exhibitions every three months. Institutions wishing to borrow exhibitions then contact the producers directly. The Crafts Council acts as a central clearing house.

There appear to be no parallel organisations to support science and technology. The travelling exhibitions which have been produced in science have been designed either by individual museums,

74

notably the Science Museum in London, by government departments, or by commercial organisations for promotional purposes. There is no formal means of letting others know about the exhibitions produced by science museums even if they are available for loan. This lack of a national body to fund, co-ordinate and encourage the production of science and technology exhibitions is the greatest obstacle to the provision of such exhibitions over which we have any control.

The last factor to consider is the use of the art exhibition as a means of communicating research. It is of course the case that a science or technology exhibition requires a considerable amount of research in its preparation, but that research is usually concerned with the tools, products, personalities or processes of science rather than the science itself. Apart from the natural sciences, there is little actual scientific research going on in museums which leads to exhibition.

The past

The Circulating Exhibition Scheme centred on the Science Museum was the most ambitious attempt to date to produce exhibitions able to travel anywhere within the UK and indeed beyond.

The scheme was proposed by the Standing Commission on Museums and Art Galleries (now the Museums and Galleries Commission) in 1963. Their recommendation was approved by the Treasury and the Department of Education and Science. Funds were made available and building began in April 1964.

The exhibitions were designed on a modular system of tubular steel frames to ease transportation, and were aimed at a wide target audience, although GCE O-level students were seen as a priority. The content of the exhibitions was biased heavily towards the physical sciences in order to counteract the perceived neglect of these subjects in the provinces. Working demonstrations of physical principles were emphasised. The exhibitions toured provincial museums using the recently formed Area Museum Councils for liaison with the local museums. The costs to the host museum, mainly made up of transport from the previous local venue, were kept low.

The scheme was enormously popular: the emphasis on working exhibits and push-buttons appealed to a wide audience. At its height the scheme employed approximately 15 people in

addition to the input from other staff at the Science Museum. The number of exhibitions grew to more than 50 covering all aspects of the physical sciences using an admirable blend of historic and scientific information. The scheme continued to be seen as a success for a number of years.

There is a lot to be learned from the history of the scheme. In the 1980s it no longer attracted the same level of funding, and consequently there was little attempt made to update existing exhibitions or to introduce new ones. The entire scheme was transferred to Tyne and Wear Museums in the early 1980s with a view to circulating the existing exhibitions without update. At this stage the scheme employed two or three technicians. As time went on the exhibitions began to show their age. Light-emitting diodes and liquid crystals were shown as a brand new technology, when in fact they had become common. The *Holograms* exhibition was another example which now looks a little embarrassing. The scheme is currently under review and is unlikely to continue, at least in its present form.

Apart from the Science Museum effort, touring exhibitions have been largely restricted to the biological sciences. Most of these have been shown in only a few museums because there is no mechanism to alert potential hosts to the existence of available exhibitions. The more successful examples have tended to be large-scale exhibitions looking at popular subjects such as dinosaurs.

In addition to museums, travelling exhibitions are provided by large industrial concerns or occasionally government departments. For example, British Gas have produced two or three exhibitions which have toured extensively in museums. While these have obviously been linked to the work of the gas industry and are primarily a means of promoting the company, they have also covered a number of fundamental scientific phenomena. There is a danger that exhibitions produced by industrial concerns might attempt to paint a rosy view of the company and its activities. I should stress that this was certainly not the case with the exhibitions from British Gas.

Government departments have on occasion produced exhibitions promoting some new initiative. A good example is the *Information Technology* exhibition which was seen in a number of museums during Information Technology year in 1982. This exhibition looked at all aspects of the information technology revolution, and contained a number of hands-on exhibits, now fast becoming an essential feature of exhibitions concerned with science and technology.

The future

Inevitably any proposals concerning new directions have resource implications, and now is not a good time to be seeking additional funds. If, however, travelling exhibitions are to fulfil their potential as a means of promoting the public understanding of science, then additional resources must be made available.

The success of the Science Museum Circulating Exhibition Scheme leads me to believe that it should form a model for the first strand of a two-part strategy. A national scheme should be introduced which would produce, circulate and update a series of travelling exhibitions. The subject matter for such exhibitions should be chosen with regard to the needs of the national curriculum and should concentrate on conveying scientific principles primarily through their applications. The funding for such a venture should be drawn from a combination of central government grants and funding from industry. The exhibitions themselves would be produced by a central research and production base in an existing organisation, possibly a museum. The central agency should also be able to fund other organisations or individuals to produce exhibitions conforming to an agreed brief. In this way a wide range of expertise would be involved in the scheme. The total number of exhibitions would be unlikely to reach the levels of the previous scheme. The emphasis should be on high-quality exhibitions using a mix of available interpretive techniques, including audio-visual and interactive exhibits.

The second strand of the strategy is to set up a central clearing house for travelling science exhibitions. This would alert both potential producers and hosts to the possibilities of co-operation. In parallel with this, a mechanism for offering funds to museums to cover the additional costs of modifying an exhibition to travel would need to be instituted. The funding aspect would be best administered through the Area Museum Councils with the additional funds being made available to the Area Councils by the Museums and Galleries Commission. Choosing an agency to act as the central clearing house is not simple. A suitable organisation not directly concerned with museums would be COPUS, or perhaps the British Association for the Advancement of Science, or indeed any national scientific or technological institution. If a museum body were to be chosen it would seem logical that the Museums and Galleries Commission should take on the job, with information relating to co-operative ventures being collected through the Area Museum Councils.

Conclusions

It is clear that the sciences lag a long way behind the arts in the availability of travelling exhibitions. It is also clear that such exhibitions could be an effective means of tackling the public understanding of science. The quality of museums' collections and their access to other museums' collections and exhibitions puts them in a position of strength. It must also not be forgotten that science museums are probably the only scientific institutions that are open to the public and indeed attract them in large numbers. This clears the first hurdle in promoting the public understanding of science – putting science and the public together. Museums also have access to education, design, and interpretation specialists as well as curatorial expertise. It is the combination of these skills which could lead to the production of travelling exhibitions providing enlightenment and entertainment. The key requirements of such exhibitions include relevance to the national curriculum, use of popular subjects such as the environment, and use of a wide variety of interpretive techniques.

In order to improve the situation for travelling exhibitions the following steps must be taken: funding must be provided for a national touring science exhibition scheme to be set up and sustained; and a clearing house must be established.

A scheme set up according to this framework would provide a cost-effective means of making a valuable contribution to the public understanding of science. Indeed there may have been no need to produce a paper such as this had the funding and momentum of the original circulating scheme been maintained.

Current practice

The role of the object in technical museums: the Conservatoire National des Arts et Métiers

Dominique Ferriot

Precursor of the technical museum in Europe, the Conservatoire des Arts et Métiers was founded in Paris in 1794, under the impetus of the Abbé Grégoire. A deposit for machines, models, tools 'newly invented or improved', the Conservatoire was to be a place of demonstration where craftsmen came to exhibit whatever bore the 'stamp of usefulness', and where technical artists, regularly appointed by the institution, prepared meticulous copies of good models.

The Museum – if one can refer to it as such – was, at the time, a workshop-museum, open to all those wishing to improve or enrich their knowledge. This educational aim was to develop at the same time as more structured teaching methods throughout the nineteenth century: the material trace of this is to be seen today in the rail which still runs through the Museum's rooms, a reminder of how exhibits were regularly transported towards the lecture halls by means of small trucks.

However, the deposit of inventions and technical models was to come to a halt at the beginning of the twentieth century. The accelerated rhythm of technical progress, the difficulties encountered by museum collections in trying to keep up with scientific and technical advances, the impossibility of carrying out demonstrations to explain many more abstract pieces of data, the full understanding of which was indispensable to the teaching of science, all these factors contributed to widening the gap between lecture hall and museum. The museum-workshop gradually became the museum-collection. Now, that gap is becoming narrower once more.

Today, the Musée des Arts et Métiers boasts a collection of over 80,000 original objects, most of which are unique exhibits of worldwide renown. Pascal's calculating machines, Foucault's pendulum, Lavoisier's laboratory, Cugnot's *Fardier*, Blériot's aeroplane, Volta's battery or the Lumière brothers' camera, to mention but a few of the Museum's *Mona Lisas*, have all acquired the status of technical works of art, prohibiting any kind of excessive or careless handling. How could one imagine attempting the water synthesis experiment in the original flask used by Lavoisier, or going down the Champs Elysées in the very first automobile dating from 1770? The demonstration or running of machines which have become historical objects is mostly carried out via the reconstruction of models, audio-visual displays or special representations. Yet the end result can vividly recall that initial emotion. Consequently, when recreating the atmosphere of Robertson's phantasmagorical shows at the end of the eighteenth century, there is no need to use the exhibits themselves. A show designed using today's technical resources, based on the marvellous images to be found on magic lantern plates, is able to stimulate the imagination whilst revealing works which filled the crowds at the Palais Royal with admiration during the French Revolution.

We can see how historical collections can be presented; should we also ask whether they are of use in the broadening of scientific and technical knowledge? The Ministry of Education in France considers it worthwhile upgrading and redisplaying the remarkable collections of the Musée des Arts et Métiers in an attempt to develop a technical culture by providing informative and meaningful displays and access to reserve collections for researchers while also developing relations with industry and with education. The objects in the Museum have been neglected for several decades and are now held in unsuitable conditions. The exhibition rooms are unable to display the treasures of the collections in the way they merit. The Museum will therefore be completely restored for the bicentennial of its opening in 1994.

'No imagination without memory', wrote Diderot in his *Encyclopédie*. This is the very cornerstone of any culture which operates via a system of accumulation, selection, and invention. Why deprive ourselves of the creativity inherent in the machines of which we are guardians? How could we fail to rediscover, through them, the periods in history which designed, used, and developed them? Even in cases where our own technology has no further point of reference with regard to an antique model, the spirit of invention and the creative process still perceptible in those models are a unique source of information, as well as pleasure and shared emotion.

In France, where technical education is today sadly neglected, as the current lack of production engineers and skilled workers is there to prove, the revival of the technical museum is a means of contributing to the rehabilitation of a technical culture based on know-how, a culture which is both manual and intellectual and highlights not only our technical heritage but also our capacity to innovate and develop new tools, new products.

Through its role as an indispensable instrument in this technical culture, the Museum's legitimacy is confirmed. Even so, it cannot accomplish everything. We should not expect it to replace school, perform better than TV, develop a critical atttitude in the same way as an analytical journal can do, or all of these things at once. We, as museum people, have the good fortune to encounter the force of history in our day-to-day work. To make objects speak, such is our principal mission. To take part in the development of scientific and technical culture, but also to bear witness to the lives of the men and women who created the works we conserve, thereby contributing to the enrichment of culture as a whole. The object in a technical museum can reveal more than scientific principles.

These several aims are to be fulfilled in the Museum through a major rethinking of the exhibition areas. Seven major themes will be looked at in depth both chronologically and with an emphasis on key ideas. The themes are based on current collection divisions: the scientific instrument, materials, building, communications, transport, energy and mechanics. However, these will be supplemented by areas placing the different technologies in perspective and demonstrating their interdependence while also providing references to other sources of information (including industrial partners). Presentations of modern technologies developed in co-operation with companies will make sure that the Museum is up to date. Links with industry and with education will result in a living museum.

In order to help make objects speak, educational workshops will be set up near the temporary exhibition areas to welcome classes and groups. Returning to its origins as a workshop-museum, there will also be a focus on demonstration by competent and well-trained staff. The Museum services will provide a link between the historical collections and the world today.

The way certain artists have adapted the use of technical objects – the works of Louise Nevelson based on wooden models for casting are an example – also serves to reveal the living connections between all forms of culture. 'All the arts have points of contact', said the Abbé Grégoire, founder of the Conservatoire des Arts et Métiers, in 1794. The renovation of his museum, on the very site where it was established, the former Abbey of Saint-Martin-des-Champs, provides an excellent illustration of the unique relationship between science and art which represents the very foundation of technical museology.

Dreams and nightmares: science museum provision in Britain

Gaynor Kavanagh

I have expectations of science museums. I expect not to understand them. I expect a visit to leave me feeling alienated, confused and exhausted. Should the museum concerned also be a museum of technology, my heart hits my boots. The problem may be that I am not a stereotypical visitor. Being neither a scientist, science curator, 10-year-old boy, closet train-spotter nor retired engineer, I suspect my chances of finding in such places the pleasures of contemplation and enlightenment generally associated with museum visiting are thin to say the least. In short, my search for personal contact with science in science museums is often futile and always depressing.

But these negative reactions are balanced by high expectations of the potential of science museums, which I feel is (with important exceptions) largely untapped. This potential lies as much in the subject itself as in the possibilities of display. It seems necessary to keep on repeating that science and technology saturate our lives: the conscious use of science determines our present and future. More than anything, our understanding of science influences how we want or are prepared to allow our society to develop. In the empowerment of our understanding, in the development of debate, in the expansion of our awareness of the principles, issues and consequences of science, the science museum has a role and responsibility unparalleled, at this moment, in other museum fields.

I do not hold with the view that our society will be remembered principally for its great technological advances, its mammoth strides in the field of science. Our failure to grasp the implications and the costs of such developments, both human and environmental, are more likely to be an outstanding feature of our collective record. It seems we are a society capable of great art, poetry and acts of compassion, at odds with itself over the deployment of scientific and technological developments. In particular, we are a society capable of refusing understanding, of abdicating responsibility to others, and of avoiding the issues even when they are blatantly obvious.

Science museums appear to distance themselves from an active role in the debate. Where efforts are seen to be made, such as in the *Global Ecology* exhibition (1991) at the Natural History Museum, London, there is a lack of restraint close to abandonment. In its advertising, the Natural History Museum claimed the exhibition was about 'the most important debate in the world today'. But the absence of both coherent content and original thought, and an apparent reluctance to engage in the debate, exposed the exhibition as a sham, a token gesture, a pointless electronic parade.[1]

There must be many reasons why science in museums is so sterile, so devoid of critical edge and creative energy (I am talking about more here than the dynamism and flash of exhibition graphics). To understand this, both inside and outside influences need to be taken into account.

Inside the museum, curators hold on tightly to traditions. The choices made and the options taken are affected by: a residual (although increasingly challenged) faith in the incompetence of the public to understand science; uncertainty (even indecision) about when to use an original object and when to use graphics and audio-visual devices to get across an idea; and awareness of the sponsor, governing body and the necessity of securing the next grant. Even when a more enlightened view prevails, the legacies of past curatorship, such as 'power halls' built for permanence like that in the Welsh Industrial and Maritime Museum in Cardiff, and unrepresentative collecting, seriously reduce the capacity of a museum to change or enter into more relevant provision.

Outside the museum, the uneasy state of science in Britain, the demoralisation of university science through lack of funding, increasing emphasis on the role of the private sector and the gradual withdrawal of public funds, all contribute to a climate that makes museums happier to focus on selected past successes than present realities. However, not all outside influences are negative ones. The development of science within the national curriculum has meant that museums (not just science museums) are looking at the ways collections can be used and exhibitions developed to meet local and regional educational needs within the field of science (look at, for example, work in education undertaken at the Museum of Science and Industry, Manchester.[2])

To move science museums forward requires as much an opening of the mind to new perspectives and questions too long neglected, as an opening of the heart to the costs of our apathy and the effects of outmoded traditions. Science museums need to discover the kind of places they have become. There are many features that are worthy, important and necessary. There are others which are not. Analysis of the range of collections, extent of documentation, and directions in fieldwork and research could well be illuminating. What are the omissions? How large are the gaps? What kind of world is represented in the collections? Further, an analysis of how science museums relate to the public they claim to serve is revealing. This is the method I shall use in this paper. It should be noted that research into museum communication and museum audiences is now very active and important contributions are being made to our understanding.[3]

Exploring museums for their hidden agendas, their unwitting testimony, their coded, partial (often male) views of the world, is improving our appreciation of how the museum is constructed. We acknowledge that no museum is innocent, that museums make visible our myths, that they hold the stories we tell ourselves about ourselves, and that they exist in a world saturated by ideology and therefore cannot be neutral. In contrast, exploring museums for their conscious agendas, their deliberately constructed messages, for the exchange of experience and meaning between the visitor and the museum, is leading to greater understanding of the potential of museums to challenge, stimulate and create meaning. Between the hidden and the conscious agendas there is a tension and it is here that the greatest force for change and for relevant, effective provision lies.

Museums are different from all other expressive media. The visitor moves around the objects and the space provided, rarely uses the design in the way the professionals intended, and both creates and exchanges meanings in very individual ways. Sheldon Annis has argued that the 'meaning of a visitor's experience depends on the choice of movement among stationary symbols'.[4] This is, in part, true. The movement to and within the museum makes the museum experience (which may be

good, bad, or indifferent). This theory, however, omits recognition of the social, cultural and intellectual factors which mediate and help form the experience itself. When we visit museums, there is much more involved than our immediate responses to what is on offer.[5]

Annis' idea of movement is an interesting one. He proposes that:

> in thinking about how visitors distil meaning from the museum's terrain and the symbols in their paths, it is important to imagine "scripts" or symbolic engagements occurring simultaneously at more than one level. These levels of object-viewer interaction can be thought of as spaces.[6]

He identifies three spaces – dream, pragmatic and cognitive – and it is under these three headings that I would like to examine science museums further.

Dream space

The dream space Annis discusses is the personal level at which we encounter the museum, 'a field of sub-rational image formation'. In his view of museum dream space, there is a 'flow of images and meanings – highly personal, sometimes lulling, sometimes surprising, more or less conscious: "I like this", "I don't like this", "I don't care about that", "I know this", etc.'[7]

In science museums, the dreaming space has a kind of surrealism. There is little connection between a piece of scientific equipment or a gleaming engine and the material world experienced daily. Maybe the connections are hidden, only available with some form of assistance. Therefore not many visitors can look upon *Parsons Combine Reaction Turbine* (1884) coupled to his high-speed dynamo and murmur 'I really like that' or 'this has meaning for me'. The best we can do is lateral leaps into 'this reminds me of', and 'this looks like a ...'. The personal affective links and cognitive associations, found more readily in social history museums and sometimes art galleries, are there in science museums, but require the visitor to make a commitment to engage, to work with the museum in the interpretive processes. This stretches the communicative role of the museum to its limits.

For example, the exhibition *Michael Faraday and the Modern World* at the Science Museum, London, held a lot of meaning for me as a visitor as I once prepared some research on his early career. I anticipated, and, with a feeling of satisfaction, found on display, the frictional electricity machine made when he was still a bookbinder's apprentice, one of his commonplace books and, of course, the induction ring. The gestalt of my memory provided the pieces I immediately needed. I used the labels, where they allowed, to fill in the bits I could not make sense of, or could only half remember. The exhibition, successfully extended through the educational work of a first-rate gallery interpreter, took on meaning, and, in an otherwise tiring day, caught my attention and interest. I lost sense of time and feelings of tiredness.

Other subjects and objects in the museum worked far less well for me on that day. My mind made 'other things' of them – shapes, colours, sounds – merging and separating as I chose, according to the agenda I set. The patterns which formed were determined by me as an individual and no museum (thankfully) can anticipate the individuality of its visitors. It may be something which needs to be acknowledged. It is the dreaming part of the visit that can add the magic or misery. Perhaps it is sufficient that museums allow space for dreaming, even:

> unguarded fantasies flying to far
> memories tumbling like sweets from a jar.[8]

The 'dream space' as a personal level of interaction is increasingly acknowledged. As fast as museums attempt to organise, route, programme, the individual chooses to disengage, set other agendas, create other messages. Radley has considered how museum visits are remembered.[9] Two forms of memory keep on returning: the personal and social aspects of the visit, and the scale and juxtaposition of objects and space in relation to the individual. We remember the extremes of things (the sight and size of material); the social and physical co-relations; the moments in the visit when our emotions were stirred (curiosity, bewilderment, humour, anger).

To develop and build a cognitive aspect to a visit requires us to allow for, even employ, the dream space. The precedent is well-established. Charles Lutwidge Dodgson – Lewis Carroll – *in Alice's Adventures in Wonderland* (1865) and particularly in *Through the Looking Glass and what Alice Found There* (1871) uses a level of metaphor, 'that life viewed rationally, and without illusion,

appears to be a nonsense tale told by an idiot mathematician'.[10] He used our ability to recognise dream space as a means of spinning critical commentary on human frailty and of dealing in the logic and mystery of mathematics. He helps us look back at ourselves by placing Alice in a world which is an inversion of our own. Like a visit to a museum, we take in his tales at whatever level we choose, through the dreaming.

Cognitive space

This is the museum as the professionals make, use and see it: rational space and designed order. Museum professionals work at the effective organisation of cognitive space through the selection, organisation and labelling of objects in such a way as to illustrate ideas. Annis describes how museum galleries are 'almost always designed around the cognitive order in the minds of curators'.[11]

In this view, then, the science curators control the cognitive order. The way that science is understood by curators is evident in display and it is this that museum visitors encounter. How this view of science and the world in which it is part is formed is an important but separate issue here. The evidence to be found in science museums suggests that the history of science is seen as a continuous success story, without break, slump, humanity, consequence. Similarly, where scientific principles are explained well, even in the better science centres, the uses of scientific principles remain undisclosed. Shine a light through a prism and a spectrum is formed ... lovely ... so what next? Where science is explained well, a kind of blandness often emerges. Where it is explained badly, little emerges at all.

To take one example, the first exhibit encountered at the Birmingham Museum of Science and Industry is a *Textile Mill Engine*, 1909. I can tell you this because I had the patience to search for information. The machine looks good, a satisfying green with brass bits. From time to time it is run, so that the engine can do whatever it is an engine needs to do. Refusing to be put off by a rising tide of tedium, I dedicated myself to finding out what it was all about. (More formally, I elected to temporarily abandon my dream space in order to engage in the cognitive space the museum sought to provide). The larger, more evident label told me, without equivocation or benefit of elucidation, that I was actually looking at a *Tandem Compound*

Corliss Condensing Engine. It then proceeded to analyse the object technically under 13 headings, grandly concluding that the object was presented by the University of Manchester. Yes, but what was it for, what did it actually do? I found another label, smaller this time. It nodded in all sorts of directions: 'the beam engines of James Watt', 'reliable power to textile mills', 'horizontal engines adopted second half of nineteenth century', 'use of engines reduced cost of products', 'rapid growth in urban areas', 'limited control of housing', 'sewerage'. In the midst of this, I discovered that the engine I was working so hard at understanding was in fact a model used not in a mill, but in the training of engineers with responsibility for much larger engines in their workplaces (presumably mills). So this was not a mill engine, it was a pretend one – someone could have told me this earlier! The above example of museum text is not unusual. Some would no doubt argue that this style of presentation is becoming a thing of the past, but I reserve judgement on this. Even in the most expertly designed of new labelling systems, the control of order and understanding will be evident, and will either elucidate or obscure.

J J Corn identifies four styles of interpretation used in the exhibition of technical objects.[12] The *celebratory* links objects to themes of individual genius, national supremacy, and technical progress (the approach evident in the Science Museum, London). The *socio-historical* style views objects in relation to specific social groups, an approach in Britain sought by social historians, but spurned by many science curators – social historians being the kind of folk who, in Neil Cossons' view, 'wear their hearts on their sleeves',[13] and generally own up to having a conscience. The third, *cultural-historical*, style, seeks to place objects within an understanding of people's values, beliefs, symbol systems, and patterns of behaviour and is currently best seen in Germany at the Rüsselsheim Museum.[14] The Birmingham example falls within the style Corn identifies as *internalist*. This is where objects are displayed according to their design, function, performance, or operating characteristics and without regard for intellectual, economic, social, political, technical and other external influences which might have shaped them, or been stimulated or affected by their existence.

When the internalist approach is carried out effectively, it helps the visitor understand machines as machines, processes as processes, experiments

as experiments. Often, however, the imagination and rigour are missing: the label/object/curator talk to themselves. It is not unreasonable to suggest that those who practice the internalist approach to object interpretation are predominately male, and, as Corn has pointed out, 'by reifying the formal and performance aspect of automobiles or other forms of technical artifacts, [they] perpetuate male power and dominations'.[15]

This is unquestionably evident in science and technology museum provision in Britain. From the choice of artefacts to the design of galleries, this form of museum maintains a gender bias that ensures that science is not shared. For example, at Newcastle Museum of Science and Technology, the display areas are prefaced by an exhibition on the museum itself. In theory, the elaboration of the museum's aim and purpose is an excellent start to a visit, briefing the visitor, raising expectations, reminding the museum itself of what it is all about. In the case of Newcastle, its purpose is made obvious – it tells us how the museum intends controlling the cognitive space.

The museum opened in 1981 with the aim of creating a museum 'worthy of past traditions and capable of stimulating inventors and workers of future generations'. Exactly what it is that inventors and future workers are being stimulated into is not made clear: compliance, or active citizenship? The motive power gallery, the first display in the new museum shows 'how man has harnessed energy from muscle power to jet power'. Good for men: so what were women doing? The use of 'man' as a generic term is neither acceptable nor excusable – even by a science museum. Reading labels in science museums is a thoroughly depressing process: 'man harnessing power', 'man the toolmaker', 'man and iron', 'the evolution of man'. If the use of the term 'man' really does mean 'humankind' or 'people' then such expressions as 'man the breast feeder', 'man the child-rearer', 'man the berry picker', 'man the homemaker', 'man the operative', 'man the organiser' would not sound so strange to the ear.[16] The use of the term 'man' in science museums usually denotes the gender-specific masculine, even though vague claims are made otherwise. It is derived from a seemingly unassailable view that the world is male. Only the object is female. Hence in the same museum the following is not untypical:

Eunice, a horizontal steam engine 1899 was used at a steam laundry in Rochdale. The museum purchased *her* in 1977. Our workshops rebuilt and restarted *her*. *She* can be seen in the motive power gallery. (Author's italics)

The object as female is no surprise in science museums. 'She' can be used, purchased, rebuilt, restarted and seen. 'She' is the acted upon, not the actor.

The fact that women were, and are, instrumental in the financing, experimentation, design, manufacture and use of so many technological and scientific developments is so much beyond the reach of many science curators as to be totally invisible in museums. Women scientists appear in the margins. For example, Marie Anne Lavoisier is known to have worked alongside her husband, Antoine Laurent Lavoisier, but it is he – not they – who is remembered for 'many important contributions to the development of chemistry'. Their portrait by Jacques Louis David (*ca* 1788) suggests an air of partnership and co-operation: Madame Lavoisier looks directly at the viewer with confidence and certainty. But in the exhibition on Faraday at the Science Museum, it is not her contribution to science that is recorded, but her two marriages, first to Lavoisier and later, after his death, to Count Rumford, founder of the Royal Institution (1799). Hence she too becomes not a subject, but an object – wife as commodity passing from one eminent scientist to another.[17]

A knee-jerk response to recognition of the gender bias inherent in science museum provision is the development of exhibitions, for example on food, thought to be of greater interest to women. Although well-intended, this perpetuates a view based on stereotypes and avoids the central concern – the opening-up of the cognitive space to both genders.

Pragmatic space

The museum visit is both a physical and social act. For some the museum is experienced 'more as a conquest than a visit'. We've done the Science Museum today! Yes, but what has it done for you and to you?

The social aspect of visiting is well-recognised.[18] Visiting museums is generally undertaken in private time and in combinations of individuals based on a family unit or networks of friends. The anticipation of the joint shared experience can be as great as the experience itself. As Annis has pointed out, 'museum going is usually a happy and social event. Being there is both purpose and product. It does not really matter whether the coins were Roman or Chinese'.[19]

In the last 15 years, museums have become much more adept at recognising the visit as a social experience. Seating, adequate access to the building, gallery plans and guides, cloakrooms, toilets, first-aid points, refreshment areas and cafeterias are now standard provision and have to be of a high quality. Provision of baby changing facilities, pushchairs or carry packs, wheelchairs, disabled access and aids for people with sight or hearing impairment are becoming more prevalent, if a little spasmodic. In sum, we have better museums where the needs of the visitor are genuinely recognised.

The most successful of museum visits seem to be those providing a good, satisfying joint experience, enhancing roles (such as those of parents and children) and allowing some movement forward in understanding. Add to this a pleasant meal in a museum restaurant and the chance to buy a worthwhile souvenir, and presumably bliss is achieved.

However, it is not always like that. Charging for museum entrance is known to be precluding adolescents and low-income families, and is discouraging casual visits, repeat visits and the selective viewing of galleries.[20] Even special deals, such as low-price season tickets, appear not to be ameliorating this effect. The costs involved (travel, food, entrance, guide books, souvenirs) put a greater pressure on people to complete the visit in one day. Planned visits with specific aims and the prospect of returning to tackle other selected galleries were characteristics of pre-charging days. Now families must 'do' museums: scalps for the belt. The results can be fairly negative: highly fractious individuals (of all ages) overdosing on the museum's cathode rays, sound systems and interactives, to the point where education is more or less prevented and social relations endangered.

If the public understanding of science is our aim, we must recognise that museums only reach a certain sector of the public. When 'museums and the public' are discussed, it is necessary to remind ourselves that the museum's public is not a cross-section of society: it is constituted by people from partial and distinctive sets of socio-economic groups. If museums do promote the public understanding of science, they do so only to those able or predisposed to visit museums.

Further, science cannot be promoted where the methods and approaches are so poorly thought-out that the objects, or the interpretive technology (it is usually one or the other), dominate over any lucid coherent point, argument, or exploration. Where the medium is offered in place of the message, museums fail.

What is the point of science in museums if you cannot get in, or are blitzed (or bored) senseless once there?

Conclusion

Annis offers the view that the magic that makes museums so attractive may lie in the flexibility with which people create their own spaces. Up to a point, people who use museums make their own meanings from what is offered to them. What should concern science museums is the scope and depth of meanings being achieved.

If we are concerned with achieved meaning, then we must go back and ask what science museums are for. What are they aiming to provide by storing up the material gathered in the name of science and technology? What kind of 'transformation' or 'extension' of understanding is their ultimate purpose? If the real answer is that they exist because they exist, then no merit can be derived from them. But if they do in fact exist to promote understanding, then some critical examination is required.

To empower the visitor with greater understanding is one of the most worthy aims a museum can have. For science museums to achieve this, there needs to be a conscious move forward in the content and quality of provision. Some creativity, humanity, humour, honesty, discussion, and a little humility would not go amiss.

Notes and references

1 Coles, A, 'Through the looking glass', *Museums Journal* (August 1991), pp20-1
Insley, J, 'Environment vs technology?', *Museums Journal* (September 1991), p16
2 *Independent* (24 October 1991)
Hooper-Greenhill, E, *Museum and Gallery Education* (Leicester: Leicester University Press, 1991).
3 See for example the papers in the two volumes which arose from the conference organised by the Department of Museum Studies, University of Leicester, *Breaking New Ground*, in April 1990:
Kavanagh, G (ed), *Museum Languages: Objects and Texts* (Leicester: Leicester University Press, 1991)
Kavanagh, G (ed), *Museums Profession: Internal and External Relations* (Leicester: Leicester University Press, 1991)
4 Annis, S, 'The museum as a staging ground for symbolic action', *Museum*, 151 (1986), pp168-71
5 Lawrence, G, 'Rats, street gangs and culture: evaluation in museums', in Kavanagh, G (ed), *Museum Languages*, pp9-32
6 Annis, p169
7 Annis, p169
8 Joan Baez, *Winds of the Old Days*, 1974
9 Hooper-Greenhill, E, 'A new communication model for museums', in Kavanagh, G (ed), *Museum Languages*, pp47-62
Radley, A, 'Boredom, fascination and mortality: reflection upon the experience of museum visiting' in Kavanagh, G (ed) *Museum Languages*, pp63-82
Radley, A, 'Artefacts, memory and a sense of the past', in Middleton, D, and Edwards, D (eds), *Collective Remembering* (London: Sage, 1990)
10 Gardner, M, *The Annotated Alice* (Harmondsworth: Penguin, 1970)
11 Annis, p170
12 Corn, J J, 'Tools, technologies and contexts: interpreting the history of American technics', in Leon, W, and Rosenzweig, R, *History Museums in the United States* (Urbana and Chicago: University of Illinois Press, 1990), pp237-61
13 Cossons, N, 'Class, culture and collections', in Kavanagh, G (ed), *Museums Profession*, p23
14 Schirmbeck, P, 'The museum of the city of Rüsselsheim' *Museum*, 33, 1 (1980), pp35-50
15 Corn, p241
16 Anon, *Adams Ancestors; Eve's In-laws: Sexual Relations and Man's Place in Evolution, Schooling and Culture*, (London: ILEA, 1980), pp57-61
17 Other eminent female scientists are mentioned by the Science Museum in its displays. Unlike their male counterparts, however, their

marriages are recorded. A label on the career of Professor Kathleen Lonsdale contains a sentence: 'she continued her work on X-ray crystallography after her marriage to Thomas Lonsdale in 1927'. What else would anyone expect from such a woman?

18 McManus, P, 'Making sense of exhibits', in Kavanagh, G (ed), *Museum Languages*, pp35-46

McManus, P, 'It's the company you keep ... the social determination of learning-related behaviour in a science museum', *International Journal of Museum Management and Curatorship*, 6 (1987), pp263-70

McManus, P, 'Good companions ... more on the social determination of learning-related behaviour in a science museum', *International Journal of Museum Management and Curatorship*, 7 (1988), pp37-44

19 Annis, p170

How Eureka! The Children's Museum responds to visitors' needs

Gillian Thomas

The purpose and function of a children's museum is often a cause for doubt and discussion, even among museum professionals, in the UK. Toys, dolls, prams, the paraphernalia of childhood, even stuffed children are suggested as some of the likely contents. Over 200 exist in the USA, and the first, the Brooklyn Children's Museum, opened almost 100 years ago. While countries as different as Venezuela, India, Japan and New Zealand also have such institutions, the specific nature of a children's museum is often unappreciated. England has made a substantial contribution to the development of discovery methods of learning, both in schools, museums, and science centres. Spaces such as the children's gallery in the Science Museum in London, opened over 50 years ago, attest to an interest in providing activities for children. However, no museum devoted to creating interactive exhibitions specifically for the primary school age group exists.

Eureka! The Children's Museum will open in Halifax, West Yorkshire, in 1992. At the centre of a 12.5 acre site, the new 4,500m² building has been designed to house exhibitions created specifically for the target public of children aged 6 to 12 and will also be of interest in its own right, as the biggest exhibit on the site. This will be the first phase of a development which aims to establish a centre for informal learning, specifically devoted to the needs of children and all those adults who are involved in their care. Today, a year after the beginning of the final design and construction phase, Eureka! is a completed building shell, surrounded by a morass of mud. Some exhibition construction has begun and designs for the rest are nearing completion. By the time this paper is published, Eureka! will have been tried and tested by the public. For the moment our intentions are clear, our development methods are established, and the programme is well under way. A small team of determined professionals is working under considerable pressure to bring this project to fruition. How well we will succeed remains to be seen; this paper outlines our methods and rationale and gives some anecdotal evidence of the help we are receiving at all stages of the development from our future public, the children for whom this museum is intended and who have also made it possible.

What exactly is a children's museum?

A children's museum could mean many things: the public often perceive it to be about childhood, but it could also be devoted to encouraging children to collect and present. However, in reality the focus of a children's museum is different: it aims to present information to its target public of children in a manner which will enable them to make optimum use of it and encourage them to acquire pleasure in learning. The exhibitions are created by adults, for children. The creative process involves children by consulting them, to ensure that both the content and the educational approach are appropriate. The autonomy of the individual to learn how he or she pleases is emphasised.

A children's museum is a non-elitist institution, aiming to be accessible to all members of the public, and integrating people with disabilities wherever possible. It is also a meeting point for all those concerned with children and their future, whether parents, teachers, child care professionals, or industrialists. Each of these has a different interest in children and their development. Parents see their children as unique individuals, whereas teachers and other child care professionals also assess them relative to their peer group. Industrialists are interested in children both as present and future consumers and as potential members of a work force. Each has an interest in encouraging children to acquire a lifelong enthusiasm for learning and each can gain from increasing knowledge of children and their development. A common interest in helping children to prepare for the future can unite these seemingly diverse strands of society.

Exhibitions in children's museums are characterised as hands-on, multi-sensory. Inheriting and synthesising different but related educational approaches such as Dewey, Montessori, and

Froebel, an emphasis has been placed on learning by doing, in a framework constructed by the individual. The influence of Piaget in analysing the different stages of children's development has been fundamental to the development of this specific educational approach. While much debate has focused on at what age different levels may occur, the demonstration of varied strategies for thinking at different ages has led at the very least to a simplification of the material presented, in terms, for example, of the number of variables to be included in any one exhibit. This awareness of the thinking processes has influenced both the criteria for selection of exhibits and the type of presentation.

Children's museums, which have in the USA been at the forefront of research into how learning happens in an informal context, have not stood still. Recent developments into learning strategies and styles, and in particular Gardner's concept of multiple intelligences, are areas which are currently of interest. As children's museums are involved in the process of learning, rather than in the specific content, so the questions which evaluation has to answer are more difficult to analyse. Questions to be studied include whether long-term curiosity is stimulated, the knock-on effect of interest in other related areas to themes explored during a visit, and how the autonomy of the individual has been increased. None of these is easily investigated.

The criteria for selection of the contents of a children's museum may be diverse. Not being, in general, related to collections, the exhibitions can treat any subject which is considered of relevance and interest to its target public. Themes linked to the daily life of children, opportunities for exploring the fringes of their experience, or deepening their understanding of phenomena which have been experienced rather than explored underlie many of the themes presented. In all cases the need to present information in an environment is an essential aspect of the exhibition policy. Unlike science centres, which tend to present a phenomenon for exploration and then lead on to an application, in a children's museum, the subject for investigation is presented in a context, which encourages further exploration and can lead to a scientific principle, but rather as an explanation than as a starting point for an investigation. The surroundings of the object or activity are also of great importance for their affective influence; the creation of an unforgettable emotional experience

helps learning to occur, and the information is stored in this context. Fields of study are not separated; historical, technological and sociological threads may run in parallel through an exhibition, in order to generate a rich environment for learning. Structure and content are embedded in a context, designed to create a holistic learning experience. The visitors, young or old, are free to pick and choose those elements which are appropriate for them at the time. None the less, while a choice is offered, the content is not hidden but made explicit throughout the exhibition. Prior knowledge is not assumed; the content is defined relative to the current position and interests of the target public.

The selection of themes is, however, related to the style of presentation. From the vast array of possible exhibition ideas, spanning, for example, the whole school curriculum and daily life, a selection is made not just on the basis of interest or relevance for children, but also on whether the subject can best be treated by the style of presentation proposed. While in theory there is no subject that could not be developed into an interactive exhibition, in practice, some subjects may be more appropriately presented as a film or only with computer programmes. While exhibitions in children's museums use all available media for presenting their themes, a choice is often made which reflects the suitability of the subject for a hands-on treatment.

Children's museums claim to be museums mainly on the grounds that they are, with traditional museums, custodians of learning, devoted to encouraging the general public, in an informal manner, to gain pleasure in acquiring knowledge. Many have collections, but, while children's museums follow standard practice in their acquisition, care, and disposal of these, the collections are considered as a tool rather than being the justification of the organisation. Objects are often acquired only for handling, and are generally integrated into the presentation, rather than being the theme itself. This is an area where the practices in traditional and children's museums are converging. Many small children's museums originally contained no objects. The importance of handling real artefacts in acquiring understanding, and the emotive impact these can have is being increasingly realised in children's museums. At the same time, traditional museums are moving towards presenting their objects in a context, rather than as objects of intrinsic interest in their own right. However, due to the emphasis on touching and handling, the possibilities of using real objects rather than facsimiles is limited in children's museums. The budgetary problems associated with collection management is an additional reason for the reluctance of many children's museums to accord collections a high priority in their development plans. They are an important facet of the panoply of resources offered, but have to be assessed as a learning tool, rather than for their own intrinsic value.

The national curriculum is of considerable importance to a children's museum. As a meeting place for the family and the school, the museum aims not only to make its presentations relevant to the national curriculum, but also to offer parents assistance in understanding its implications for their children. Where their children are, what they will be learning, how they may approach particular subjects, are all of interest to parents. Combined with information on children's ideas about the exhibition themes, these form a resource which enables the parent to make better use of the visit and to fulfil the role of mediator with greater ease.

The development process

At the beginning of the development process, it is essential to determine the existing knowledge of the target public, and whether or not the proposed content is of interest to them. For the majority of themes proposed, there is rarely sufficient evidence available as to children's ideas. There is the additional disadvantage that such information, when it is available, is also only relevant for the areas where the research was carried out, as it is heavily influenced by the local culture. The effect of the existence of a national curriculum can standardise the accessibility of knowledge, but can also make it difficult to transfer research results from one country to another. For example, in developing a computer database game for the opening of the Inventorium, the children's space at the Cité des Sciences et de l'Industrie, La Villette, Paris, it was proposed to use the adjective 'retractable', as a description of cats' claws, as opposed to those of dogs. If this comparison of claws had not been in the French national curriculum, it is extremely unlikely that it could have been used by many children, either as a word, or as a criterion for selection. As, however, it was, this fact can be used

by a majority of seven-year olds in choosing criteria for defining differences between animals.

Working with children poses an additional difficulty: conventional techniques of interviews and questionnaires rarely give valid results. Children have an inordinate desire to please. The necessary presence of the accompanying adult can inhibit both the child and the interviewer. Children's oral presentation skills are only developing. While collaborative adults may well distort their views in an attempt to correspond to the interviewer's perceived requirements, children may have difficulty focusing on the subjects under discussion, as their interests and the important aspects of a visit are, for example, more related to interaction with their friends than to the exhibition themes. This is also true for adults, but they conceal it better.

Methods which are familiar to children from their everyday lives have to be developed. An initial feel for an exhibition theme or area can sometimes be established by discussions in groups, followed by visits with children. This technique is used by toy manufacturers to establish potential interest for a proposed toy such as a fire station or garage. It is particularly appropriate for the *Living and Working Together* theme at Eureka!, which relies on role play and creating an environment to interest children in the hidden aspects of the everyday world, and in the exchanges that occur in society. A set around a town square presents a house, a shop, a factory, a bank, a garage, excavation, and a recycling centre for exploration. To gauge the interests of different areas, visits and discussions were carried out with a variety of school groups. Some unexpected interests were revealed, such as relative pay levels of different staff members in the shop, or curiosity about whether the manager had ever been sued. Dealing with contracts and mortgages was the ambition of one 10-year old on being asked what she would like to do most in a bank.

Unexpected lack of knowledge were also revealed. Some eight-year olds had no concept of what a factory might be or do. In general, the range from lack of knowledge to detailed information was wider than anticipated. This has considerable implications for the activities to be developed: it is essential to start from very simple questions (what is a factory?) and yet offer in-depth information and games for those visitors who already have considerable knowledge.

Information about concepts underlying a theme can also be gathered from discussions. Questions such as, 'Do you do any work?', 'Why do people work?', and 'What work would you like to do?' are among those discussed with children. Initial information was obtained from the *Primary Enterprise* pack, a teacher support pack aimed at raising teachers' awareness of children's concepts of the world of work. Similar studies in Halifax have revealed that while 'you get paid for it' was seen as the main reason for going to work, overcoming boredom, learning to do things well, and making people happy were also considered important.

Peer group pressure is very strong among primary age children and research methods that restrict its influence are valuable. Write and draw techniques encourage children in the security of their class or a quiet museum space to respond individually either to questions or situations. This can give valuable information, and is important in those areas where children may be embarrassed or hesitant about expressing their ideas. It is particularly useful for children using English as a second language. Both drawing and writing may need help from a friendly adult, to label an unclear picture or to spell words. It is the child that decides on the content and only asks for help when necessary. There is no right or wrong answer. Initial ideas of the questions or scenario can be chosen after a few small trials.

This technique was used extensively in developing the exhibitions at the Inventorium. For the majority of the themes chosen, there was little existing information about children's ideas. Investigations included preliminary work on the communications exhibition, some investigations into colour, and work on the creation of educational materials to accompany the exhibitions. The studies were carried out by the educational staff, headed by Dr Jack Guichard, with the assistance of trainees on work experience. University research projects were integrated into the programme. This approach has been fundamental in the development of the exhibition themes at Eureka! Dr Tim Caulton, Head of Education and Interpretation, has established a programme of development working with 12 schools in Calderdale (the metropolitan borough which includes Halifax). These schools are both urban and rural and represent a wide range of socio-economic backgrounds.

Following on from initial discussions and visits, areas requiring more detailed investigations have

been identified, and the results are being used as the basis for the work on creating the educational support materials to be integrated into the exhibitions, as well as the additional materials to be provided for schools.

For the *Me and My Body* theme, some substantial research work was already available. This theme offers visitors the chance to find out more about themselves, how their bodies work, and promotes healthy lifestyles, encouraging children to take an increasingly responsible attitude to their own health and safety. Considerable use has been made of the *Health for Life* research, carried out at Southampton University, with funding from the Health Education Authority. Noreen Wetton, current Director and member of the original research team, is continuing to act as an adviser to Eureka! *Health for Life* uses write and draw techniques, as well as questionnaires. Some of the simple questions which have been found to correspond to children's queries and areas of interest have been developed into sections of the exhibition. For other areas, where no available research has been found, more detailed studies are being carried out. Gail Richards, of the Calderdale Health Education Authority, with advice from Noreen Wetton, has been working with the Eureka! team to investigate children's ideas about growing and changing, and in particular the worries associated with adolescence. This is a sensitive theme, for which it is essential to be close to children's perceptions. Asking the children directly may reveal little; creating a scene which allows children to project their thoughts and feelings onto others gives richer results. The scene is set by inviting children to help with the writing of a book, the story of a boy and girl who are teenagers, starting to change into young adults, and both of them about to go out on their own, for the first time. Children are asked to draw either or both of them, ready to go out. Speech bubbles can be included to indicate how they feel about growing up. Children are asked to indicate how the picture shows that they are growing up.

This project is currently being carried out in schools in Calderdale. As well as giving invaluable information for the *Growing and Changing* part of the exhibition, it has been of considerable use to the schools, in evaluating the results of their educational programmes and signalling misunderstandings. It would be extremely difficult to obtain this information in a museum context. On the other hand, an exhibition which did not have this information available risks being irrelevant to children's real interests and questions. By carrying out tests in a wide variety of schools, any important cultural sensibilities can be gauged and appropriate content developed.

However much research is carried out, there is always another question which it would be interesting to ask. The limits are those of practicality: how much time and how many staff are available. This is the pragmatic approach to development; as much research as possible is carried out, given the limited time and resources. Nor should the status of the information obtained be too highly estimated. This is anecdotal evidence, rather than conclusive research results. It gives the feel, the limitations, some idea of how best to present the information. It cannot be generalised to other places, other themes or exhibitions. It is the process rather than the results which can be generalised.

Working with schools prior to opening has additional advantages in that it enables a group of self-motivated young people to be created, who will work as volunteer interpreters at Eureka! This will take time to develop, but is one of the aims of the anti-smoking policy, which is an important aspect of the *Me and My Body* exhibition. The use of peer educators has proved particularly successful at Indianapolis Children's Museum, where over 200 children are involved.

Prototype testing has long been seen as an essential stage in the development of exhibits in science centres. This method gives useful information as to the technical viability of the exhibit, the public's perception of the content, and can indicate the questions to be asked to stimulate exploration by the visitor. It does, however, have a fundamental flaw, in that the conditions for use are almost always considerably different from the final installation. The materials, colours, lighting, and graphics can give a quite different impact to an exhibit. Testing an exhibit in a school where it only has to compete with the regular programme of lessons may be a poor indication of its intrinsic interest. On the other hand, an exhibit that has successfully withstood testing at the prototype stage, and has been shown to be of interest to and understood by a wide range of visitors, will not fail when it is presented in the more favourable surroundings of a museum, supported by clear graphics. Some of the quintessential user-friendly feel of the prototype

may, however, be irreparably lost in the finished version. This is inevitable and can only be overcome by incorporating corners for children to work under supervision and with more delicate or dangerous materials.

Adults in a children's space

Most children's spaces in museums find that up to 50 per cent of their visitors are adults. Often the prime movers in deciding on the visit, adults are both the mediators for the children and can also find pleasure in learning for themselves. In a study carried out at the Inventorium, after 'helping the children', 'enjoying myself' was the most usual motivation for adults. Adults said that they read written material in the exhibition both to explain to the children and also for their own information. This study was carried out to identify adults' needs, as their importance in the learning process is evident. An unhappy or bored adult will pull a child away from an activity; an interested adult can become an expert interpreter, encouraging the child to explore further. Initially, the Inventorium had little written material, as the emphasis was on learning by doing. Adding extra information, with a reading age of 8 or 9 and accompanied by cartoon style graphics, was found to lengthen significantly the time spent by family groups on individual exhibits.

At Eureka!, emphasis is being placed on offering information and facilities which will cater for all the family. As well as background information, designed to encourage dialogue and provoke discussion and exploration, parents can discover what children may find of interest and be able to do at different ages. Encouraging adults to become more competent observers of their children will help them to make a fuller use of the resources available.

To feel comfortable in an exhibition it is important that both physical and mental needs are catered for. Many family groups contain very young children; some have elderly grandparents. Adequate seating, baby changing, and breast feeding facilities may all seem to have little educational content at first glance, but without them, the physical problems of organising the family group may interfere to such an extent that the visit is curtailed. Establishing a welcome for all the family and making the visit accessible to all is a priority.

Conclusion

When Eureka! opens, it will be a major new educational resource. It has been developed in collaboration with children and has received assistance from a wide range of specialists and individuals, who have wished to contribute towards creating a centre which aims to help children to enjoy learning. But this is just the beginning; the initial exhibitions will continue to develop and will need input from their visitors to achieve their aims. Eureka! has acquired a lease of 125 years on the site; it is to be hoped that as progress in understanding about how children learn occurs, the methods of developing exhibitions will evolve, making them increasingly effective. For the moment, a body of skills is being acquired, a methodology of development which could be applied to any target public.

Once Eureka! is established, a new challenge could be considered: how to capture the interest of adolescents and provide facilities specifically for them. The children who are helping us in developing the exhibitions now could become the designers of tomorrow.

The Museum of Science and Industry in Manchester: the local and historical context

Patrick Greene and Gaby Porter

At first sight, the Museum of Science and Industry in Manchester may appear to be misnamed: the Museum bears few of the conventional marks of science museums in its displays.[1] The curatorial staff and collections are grouped under the broad headings of industry, energy, science, air and space, and social history; the Library and Record Centre has a strong bias towards local heavy industries in its archive collections.

This orientation is not an omission of science, but rather a deliberate strategy to place science and technology in their social context. Our approach is summed up in the phrase, 'the museum of industrial society', or, more precisely, 'the museum of the industrial city'. Manchester is a city where the roles played by science and scientists have historically been enmeshed in the industrial, social, and political life of the region. For example, in studying and representing the textile industry, science and industry are inseparable: all branches of the industry use science. It has, since the nineteenth century, been employed in developing new products and machines, new dyestuffs and finishes, in monitoring and quality control. The application of science, in turn, has had profound effects on industry. The Manchester Statistical Society used science as a tool for social reform by methodically collecting data as a means of analysing and understanding social problems. It then applied science to combat those problems. The area has a rich body of scientific and technical education and expertise; we can contribute to and draw upon this as a present resource, as well as representing its past.

The approach is also appropriate to the Museum's visitors, most of whom are familiar with the regional and local context and may be connected with local industries. In 1990, 46 per cent of visitors were from the Greater Manchester area, and a further 34 per cent from Lancashire and Cheshire.[2]

Finally, the approach both reflects and contributes to the management of staff and resources in the museum. The Museum of Science and Industry in Manchester places a high priority on corporate and shared approaches to development. New methods and systems of working are tested, and, if appropriate, are implemented to achieve both task and welfare objectives.[3] The organisational structure and management of the Museum encourage integration rather than compartmentalisation; scientific and technological expertise are valued but are not privileged. In academic institutions, and in larger science museums, such an integrated approach may be hindered or obstructed by the existence of separate collection departments, and by competition between these separate specialists for resources.[4]

How do visitors encounter science?

There is little 'pure' science in the public displays and activities of the museum. Science as a set of practices and institutions is represented only in the *Microscopes* gallery. Elsewhere, the displays present an integrated account in which science is one element. For example, *Out of this World* – a gallery about space, opened in 1990 – includes space exploration and space travel, as well as popular conceptions and fictions about science and space in cinema and television drama, comics, and books. In the *Making of Manchester* gallery, which opened in 1988, science is included as one of the threads in the fabric of Manchester's cultural and intellectual, as well as industrial, history.

The Museum uses interactive exhibits to demonstrate the scientific principles underlying everyday actions: how things work. In *Xperiment!*, the Museum's interactive science centre, basic principles are explored in three main areas: energy, light and, most recently, gas. These exhibits and their effects are explained by gallery staff who also spend part of their time designing, building, and maintaining exhibits. This combination of roles provides the staff with a direct means of feeding back visitor response into the design and construction process. In *Xperiment!*, visitors learn scientific principles through hands-on experimentation, backed up by the explainers. In the galleries with long-term displays, the interactive principle is used to explain how scientific principles are put to work in industrial and social contexts. For example, interactives have been built to show how gas holders work, in the *National Gas* gallery; radiation monitoring in *Energy for the Future*; rocket propulsion in *Out of This World*. In the near future, we intend to extend this approach to develop interactive exhibits for temporary exhibitions in the Museum and, perhaps, off-site. In the long-term displays, too, demonstrators operate machines and appliances to show how they work and to explain the context of the machines to visitors. Demonstrations are given in the *Power Hall*, the *Textiles* gallery and, less frequently, in the *Machine Tool* gallery and the *National Gas* gallery. Volunteers work in the *Printing* gallery and on the locomotives and aircraft.

Through educational and public programmes, areas labelled 'science' may be brought out and developed from exhibitions and displays organised historically. The Museum Education Service (partly funded by Manchester City Council) has developed programmes which link classroom-based activities, gallery displays and *Xperiment!* exhibits to meet curriculum requirements and attainment targets in science, design and technology, and indeed in many other subjects. One teacher, whose post is funded by National Power, links such programmes with visits to local power stations. Museum staff work closely with the British Association (BA), which employs a part-time regional co-ordinator based at the Museum. Each year, around 2,000 children attend a BA Youth Section (BAYS) event organised around a theme which is linked to museum displays: space in 1990, gas in 1991, sound in 1992. The BA co-ordinator also organises other events at the Museum for BA members and general visitors, such as science shows and lectures.

In a recent initiative, the marketing, curatorial and education staff have collaborated on a series of science shows and other activities for the public. These will be developed into a broader programme of events and workshops, linked to themes in temporary exhibitions, permanent displays and collections.

The Museum's permanent galleries are developed around themes which place general histories and topics in their regional and local context. The galleries are organised in a chronological narrative which continues up to the present. In this way, the Museum acknowledges its role in public education, by providing information which assists visitors in understanding contemporary environmental and scientific issues, often with a global dimension.

Here, there are inevitable problems. The first that of committing the time and money which a truly up-to-the-minute display on contemporary issues would demand. Those areas devoted to the 'latest' news often look tired and worn and show their own history, and the history of changes in public opinion, rather than the hottest news. The second problem is that of partiality. As we stated at the beginning, our focus in the Museum is on applied science; indeed, in the context of Manchester, it is questionable whether 'pure' science exists. The Museum relies heavily on large corporate bodies for the capital funds and expert advice to develop new galleries. It is precisely these organisations which are often challenged in contemporary issues and debates. The Museum's capacity to speak independently is therefore seen by some visitors to be compromised. This is clear when we collect visitors' comments from the box in the Museum's recent, and most controversial, gallery on nuclear and renewable energy, *Energy for the Future*. However, we recognise that all funds from outside sources, whatever their nature, can give rise to suspicions of partiality; only funds earned by the Museum from its visitors are neutral in this respect.[5]

Future developments

The Museum's future development programme is closely tied into the restoration and adaptation of the 1830 warehouse. This important building, the first railway warehouse, is the only large building on the present site which remains to be developed for public use. In this next phase of development, our planned exhibition themes extend beyond production and processing to distribution, consumption, and communication. Thus, in one bay of the warehouse, we will explain the site and surrounding water, road and rail links as a focus for distribution of materials, goods and services in the area. Other broad exhibition themes under consideration, such as *Food for the City* and *Information*, will be interpreted in the context of Manchester and the region. As in existing displays, science will be an integral part of the interpretation. We wish to bring these displays up to date, too, using the techniques of journalism as suggested by Morton to debate the issues.[6]

Finally, our long-term development plans include

a resource area for public access to the collections. Linking the existing Library and Record Centre with future open storage for collections, this will provide database information on collections and relevant topics, and also offer more extensive search facilities to a wider public than we are able to provide at present. We hope to develop interactives and handling collections in the resource area to explain aspects of materials science, as well as the scientific knowledge underlying our professional practices of preventive and remedial conservation.

Notes and references

1 The Museum of Science and Industry in Manchester opened on its present site in 1983. It was based on the earlier foundation and collections of the North Western Museum of Science and Industry, formed in 1969 by staff at the University of Manchester Institute of Science and Technology (UMIST) seeking to recover the artefacts and record the buildings of the region's declining industries. The present site of the Museum incorporates the world's first railway station, terminus of the Liverpoool to Manchester railway, along with the railway viaduct and associated warehouses and freight sheds.

2 *Summary of 1990 Visitor and Public Awareness Surveys* (Manchester: Business and Market Research plc for the Museum of Science and Industry, 1991)

3 For example, the Museum's staff development scheme, introduced in 1989, links individual training to organisational and departmental goals.

4 Knight, R, 'Modern science and technology within a broader collections policy', in *Museum Collecting Policies in Modern Science and Technology* (London: Science Museum, 1991), p38

5 These issues are raised in Fox, R, 'Research and curatorship in the national science museums: a reflexion on threats and opportunities, *Impact of Science on Society*, 159 (1991), pp263-71

6 Morton, A, 'Tomorrow's yesterdays: science museums and the future' in Lumley, R (ed), *The Museum Time-Machine* (London: Routledge, 1988), p141

Asking the public what they want

Bill Brookes

In museums the key vehicle for improving the public understanding of science is the exhibition. This paper considers the process of exhibition development and suggests that the public, for whom the exhibition is intended, have to be considered and involved at every stage.

Anyone working within a museum and making a contribution to the greater public understanding of science needs to consider three very important questions: who are the 'public' that the exhibition or the museum as a whole is addressing? why is the public understanding of science important? and how can the quality of communication in exhibitions be improved?

The museum's public

A large number of people visit museums. For instance, in 1991 over 400,000 people walked through the door of the Birmingham Museum of Science and Industry. These visitors are made up of a huge variety of men and women of differing ethnic origin, disability, class, age, sexuality, level of educational achievement and scientific understanding. Can all these people be reached effectively and simultaneously? Does it make sense to try, or should individual exhibitions and displays be targeted towards specific groups within the visiting population? If so, towards whom?

There will be appropriate answers to these questions for each museum and display but it will always be necessary to be clear about the target audience for any exhibit. The target audience should be stated explicitly as part of the development brief; it will influence decisions throughout the development process.

The public understanding of science

Why is the public understanding of science important? A familiar answer to this question is that widespread scientific literacy, numeracy and technical competence are essential to our economy. Another reason is that these skills are important to the individual in that they seem to increase

confidence and the feeling of being in control in everyday life. Both these answers are valid and both are increasingly important in our technological age.

There is also a second class of answer based on the premise that science is a very significant cultural activity and a supreme example of human creativity. This is not always acknowledged as true in our society and our culture is severely impoverished as a result. Museums have a particularly important role to play in improving the understanding of the cultural significance of science. They are uniquely equipped to put science into a historical perspective and to display its achievements.

Improving the quality of communication in exhibitions

Total quality management

The theory and practice of total quality management (TQM) is well developed and applied in many manufacturing and service industries. Philip Crosby, the quality management consultant, has likened TQM to ballet.[1] For each ballet production there is a long period of rehearsal during which all the problems with staging that particular ballet with those particular performers in the chosen venue are ironed out. By the opening night, everyone knows exactly what to do (the requirements are completely specified), and every public performance is the same (the quality is consistent). He contrasts this to a football match which is different every time, no matter how much the teams practice. Crosby maintains that companies managed like a ballet production make a consistent product with minimum stress while those that are managed like a football game produce a lot of errors, unhappy customers, and pressurised staff.

The challenge is to make exhibition development more like ballet and less like football. Exhibitions are almost always 'one-offs' with the consequent danger that their development is managed on the football match model.

In order to use the lessons learned from TQM and to make exhibition development more like ballet there has to be total commitment from everybody involved to realising the aim of the exhibition. The development has to be managed on the basis of an agreed specification and rehearsal stages have to be built in to the exhibition development process.

Managing this process breaks down into three steps: defining the objectives that have to be achieved in order for the aim to be realised; translating each objective into a set of measurable requirements; and ensuring that the requirements are actually met.

Note that there is a hierarchy from aim to objective to requirement. The aim spawns several objectives each of which can be translated into a set of requirements. The requirements are the parts that are directly measurable. Thus each objective can actually be defined by its corresponding set of requirements.

For example, assume that an exhibition is being developed with the aim of improving the public understanding of an aspect of science. Further assume that the target audience has been defined. In order for the aim of the exhibition to be fulfilled several objectives will have to be met. One of these objectives is that the individual exhibits communicate to the defined audience. This objective can be translated into a set of requirements such as the optimum holding power of the exhibit, the length and reading age of the associated label, and so forth.

It is very hard to translate aims into objectives and objectives into requirements and to get it right first time. In order to achieve this, rehearsal stages need to be built in where the tools of evaluation and consultation can be brought in to help. Rehearsal opportunities exist whenever it is possible to make changes as a result of testing out some part of the exhibition. For example, these opportunities are created when members of the target audience are asked what they want to know before the detailed planning starts, when prototype exhibits are tested or summative evaluation is carried out with a view to making changes to the 'finished' exhibition.

Evaluation

The evaluation of an exhibit or exhibition is the collection and analysis of meaningful quantitative data in order to assess its worth or success. This is an important task as well as a difficult one. Much has already been written about it: see, for example, Miles *et al.*[2] There are four main types of evaluation defined by the stage of the project at which they are carried out. The main types are: front-end, formative, summative and meta-evaluation.

Front-end evaluation is carried out at the planning stage to check out ideas and concepts. The aim is to identify the concepts and level of presentation that will be appropriate to the target audience.

Formative evaluation is the evaluation of exhibit prototypes. It is used to inform the exhibit building process at a stage where it is still possible to make substantial changes to the exhibit design.

Summative evaluation is done on exhibits and exhibitions that are, in some sense, finished. It is important for two reasons. Firstly, it formalises and makes coherent the assessment of the achievement and degree of success of the event. It thus informs all future exhibit planning and development. Secondly, if the evaluation is carried out at a stage where refurbishment of the exhibits or revision of the interpretation is planned, the results can be used directly.

Meta-evaluation is the evaluation of the evaluation itself. This may seem very remote but it is very important to periodically assess the reliability of the evaluation methods used.

Evaluation can be both expensive and time-consuming and it is often impossible to implement fully the evaluation process when planning and designing an exhibition. The employment of outside consultants to carry out a rigorous, formal study may be an ideal but it is not the only sort of evaluation that can be carried out, nor the only sort that has value. It is always important to be mindful of all the stages in the exhibition development process where it is possible to implement changes and to be aware of all the informal sources of data and knowledge that already exist in the institution.

How many visitors walk through the front door every day? What comments do they leave in the visitors' book? Is it worth following any of these up? What experience do the staff, both front of house and curators, already have? How can this knowledge be captured and formalised? The important thing is to value the evaluation process and to use the available data at the appropriate time and to the greatest effect.

Within Our Power

An example of a project where informal sources of knowledge were used is in the development process of the gallery *Within Our Power* in Birmingham Museum of Science and Industry. This gallery is a radical redisplay of the Engineering Hall which is at the front of the museum and gives access to all further display areas. The gallery contains some very large and significant exhibits which it did not make sense to move but which needed to be better interpreted. Although this redisplay had been a Museum objective for some time, in the end only a single financial year was available to work up the conceptual brief and to carry the project through to physical realisation.

The aim of the redisplay is: 'to greatly improve the visual appeal, coherence and intellectual and physical accessibility to visitors of the displays in the Engineering Hall'.[3]

Among the objectives following from this aim were: 'to thin out and rationalise the exhibits to emphasise their quality and importance ...' and 'to give the visitor a much better feel for the concepts of force, work and power and an idea of how much power the visitor, as a human being, can produce.' The target audience for the redisplay is, very consciously, a non-specialist one. The outline brief specifies: 'A non-specialist general audience of both adults and children; local people and visitors. The presentation should be at a generally accessible level and gender and cultural stereotypes should be countered ...'

This target audience is very different from the one for which the gallery was originally planned in 1950: '... engineers and others, filling the gap between the workshop and the university ...'.[4]

It was a considerable challenge to move from a 'cabinet of curiosities', originally targeted at an audience with some engineering experience, to a 'front of house' display with universal accessibility. It was a particular challenge to do it within the limited time available: the best use had to be made of the knowledge and experience which already existed within the staff of the museum service. The working group developing the project deliberately included curators whose specialism was not science or technology as well as education and design staff. The group was also deliberately made up of equal numbers of women and men.

The working party members without a science or engineering background all had important skills to bring to the planning and design of the gallery but they also effectively represented the non-specialist audience during the development process. They made a vital contribution by creatively challenging assumptions and putting forward alternative viewpoints. The way that the project was managed made very clear the points at which it was possible to make changes.

The display has been designed to be as flexible as possible so that changes can be made and further interpretation added in the future. In this way it will be possible to listen to and learn from the real users of the gallery.

Learning from Service Users

The *Learning from Service Users* project is being pioneered in all departments in Birmingham City Council.[5] The project has been set up in co-operation with the Local Government Management Board and draws on experience gained in the Birmingham Social Services Department's consultation with carers in the community.

The project is about listening to users and getting close to them in order to really understand how they feel about the services provided. Within each department a specific user group is targeted and a project action team is responsible for defining and, together with some members of that user group, carrying through a project which can be achieved within six months using only existing resources. For both the staff and the users this is 'learning by doing'.

In Birmingham both the museum and the library departments have chosen to target users with learning difficulties. One of the projects carried through is a review and redesign of the signing system within the Central Library. The project team identified the signing system as something difficult to use and then went on to suggest a new design which makes it more accessible to people with learning difficulties.

If the *Learning from Service Users* approach were to be used alone as a method of evaluation, it would clearly give limited and anecdotal information. However, used in conjunction with more formal and traditional methods, it has two key strengths: it puts flesh on the bones of statistical data making the data more accessible and meaningful and making it more likely to be taken seriously; and it is actually carried through by staff at all levels in the organisation. The experiential nature of the learning gives everyone ownership of the outcomes. This feeling of ownership is a vital piece of the jigsaw of management of change necessary if museums are to be responsive to their public.

Learning from Service Users is an initiative that can and should be taken on board by museums. Used alongside formal and informal evaluation techniques it will help museums to collect good data about what their users need as well as being a vital management tool in actually responding to those needs.

Notes and references

1 Crosby, P, *The Quality Man* (BBC video)
2 Miles, R, *et al*, *The Design of Educational Exhibits* (London: George Allen & Unwin, 1982)
3 Brookes, B, *Engineering Hall Redisplay 1991/2 – Outline Brief* (Birmingham Museums and Art Gallery internal document)
4 Report from Birmingham Museums and Art Gallery Committee to full Council, June 1950
5 Trivett, S, *Learning from Service Users* (Birmingham: Birmingham City Council LSU Publications, 1991)

Visitor centres

Bringing technology to the community: Sellafield Visitors' Centre

Duncan Jackson

Science and the general public

Society within the developed world relies on a highly complex technological base and in the UK a major part of the working population is employed within large industrial concerns. Yet it is commonly asserted that science is mistrusted by the majority of the public. In particular, many of the cornerstone industries, such as energy, chemicals and pharmaceuticals have a poor image. This produces a profound paradox. A lifestyle of increasing leisure and material wealth remains highly attractive but its very basis often provokes deep-rooted fears and extreme reactions as evidenced by the almost universal organisation of local pressure groups opposed to any large industrial development.

The reasons for this prevailing attitude are complex, lying both within the domain of education and the baser instincts of emotion. It was noted by an eminent sociobiologist that phobias appear to be an innate response, impervious to the effects of education.[1] Thus, he reasoned, arachnaphobia remains prevalent in countries such as the UK although logical argument dictates that the fear cannot be supported. By contrast, phobias to cars are extremely rare, if present at all, yet road accidents are an all too common occurrence, with a sufficient fatality rate that an induced phobia could be sustained quite rationally. In much the same way, it may be noted that nuclear power generates deep-seated, irrational fear and opposition, yet its end product, electricity, is accepted almost without reservation. This despite the fact that nuclear power generation has an unrivalled safety record across the world (taking into account the well-recorded disaster at Chernobyl, USSR, in 1986), whilst in the UK alone more than 900 people have died of electrocution in the decade 1980 to 1990.[2] Perhaps part of the explanation for this clear dichotomy in attitudes was recognised by Samuel Taylor Coleridge (1772-1834) when he wrote: 'Poetry is not the proper antithesis to prose, but to science. Poetry is opposed to science'. The justification of attitudes, the primacy of emotion, even an acceptance of the irrational, are often the hallmarks of poetry, and who amongst us, even trained scientists, would wish to disown the poetic side of their soul?

Why improve the understanding of science?

It is an easily assumed arrogance amongst scientists that the opinions of the uneducated general public are an irrelevance. T H Huxley (1824-1895) appeared to justify this attitude quite succinctly when he stated: 'Science is nothing but trained and organised common sense'. From this it would follow that the understanding of science is open to all and those who choose to remain in ignorance choose also to relinquish their right to influence its path. Put thus boldly, who would wish to deny their own common sense, or the reasonableness that we should be governed by those best able to do so by virtue of their education or pre-eminence in fields which may be highly specialised. Yet, as King Lear mused, 'that way madness lies'. It opposes, quite fundamentally, the principles of democracy so hard fought for.

The Luddite Movement, of the early nineteenth century, is often derided for its implacable destruction of machinery which appeared to undermine the position of craftsmen: however the fear of loss of status and employment was deep-seated and continues through to this day. In the modern age, acronyms such as NIMBY (Not In My Back Yard) or BANANA (Build Absolutely Nothing Anywhere Near Anybody) are often used scathingly to describe opponents to industrial ambitions for expansion. Such polarisation of attitudes is a futile exercise. It is a pre-requisite both for continued fundamental research and development, and for industrial advancement, that a measure of public support should both be discernible and willing to identify its position. Making science and industry accessible to the public is thus vital, if such considered support is to be forthcoming. This means that operations must be made understandable, intentions stated honestly and benefits, as well as costs, explained clearly.

The role of the visitors' centre

Public fear or distrust is based largely on ignorance which gradually evolves into a fixation that industry is secretive. In other words, it may be reasoned, if the individual has little personal knowledge or information regarding industry then it follows that industry must be withholding the information and, since only dark matters are concealed, industry must be dangerous. Such reasoning may be erroneous, but can be very powerful.

If the principle of promoting public support for, and understanding of, industrial development is accepted, it then follows that a suitable medium for influencing opinion is required. It may be argued that such a function lies within the governmental domain of education. It may be argued equally that any self-interested proponent of a cause should be prepared to advance their own case in order to encourage support for the proposed, or existing, facilities under discussion.

In either case the obvious answer is to pour out information endlessly. This is expensive and may be counter-productive. If credibility is low to start with, the information is likely to be dismissed as untrue or, at best, of little value. More effectively, industry must offer to make the information available freely. For the majority of people, the offer alone is sufficient to allay fears and remove the need for further information. Providing this is backed up by a real service for those who wish to explore further, the cycle of mistrust can then be reversed.

Visitors' centres have become a resource employed increasingly within industry, fulfilling the three functions of education, marketing and entertainment (or community relations). The emphasis placed on these factors depends on the type of industry and its current public standing (figure 1 on page 107). Within tourism there is a clear shift towards entertainment, whilst manufacturers for the retail trade will veer towards marketing. For 'technological' industries the educational role is promoted most strongly. As a concept, visitors' centres can seem very attractive to industry. They offer a means of accommodating large numbers of visitors with minimum disruption to the workforce (and thus production), whilst maximising the home ground opportunity for high impact influencing of opinion particularly within the local catchment area.

Less attractively, visitors' centres are costly and require accurate audience targeting. Information must be correct and understandable. Descriptions of rival processes must be based on valid comparisons. Alternative views must be recognised. Presentations must not be misleading and sufficient flexibility is required to respond to topical issues. Above all, visitors' centres must seek to enlighten without dictating. This is a delicate but crucial balance and credibility can be affected by many seemingly unrelated factors such as admission charges, staff uniforms and catering standards.

Designing the exhibits

Successful exhibits in a visitors' centre do not just happen. They require creative inspiration and methodical realisation. Consideration must be given to the wide range in age and technical ability of visitors to be welcomed, and thus to the balance of detail required between interactive and passive learning displays. Information overload must be avoided, whilst nevertheless offering the enquiring mind the opportunity to think further. Providing an embracing welcome to visitors with disabilities requires particular care and should not be limited to provision of wheelchair access: those with sight or hearing difficulties must also be accommodated. Perhaps above all, it is important that the exhibition has a uniting theme which links all displays and can lead to a logical, developing, progression through the centre.

The advantages and disadvantages of nuclear power, and the reprocessing of spent fuel, have been debated through the media in great detail; covering all aspects from economics to accident scenarios. The industry as a whole now faces a review in 1994 which will determine its future within the UK. Dr Johnson once exclaimed that, 'when a man knows he is to be hanged in a fortnight, it concentrates the mind wonderfully'. It is to be hoped that the nuclear industry does not face a death sentence but the circumstances are certainly right for a concentrated approach to the future. In this context it is a fundamental belief at the Sellafield Visitors' Centre that all individuals are equally entitled to an opinion which contributes to the broader debate. The more informed that opinion, the more likely that it will be favourable to the continuation of the nuclear industry. Great importance is thus attached to conveying this information.

From the start, the designers of the Visitors'

Centre, which opened in 1988, were able to draw on the experience gained from six years of operating an earlier exhibition centre. Without advertising, the previous centre had attracted some 25,000 visitors per year. Customer response to various themes could be tested. National advertising started in 1986. The overwhelming response dictated a new centre and a new approach.

A feeling of space is created from the reception area, through each exhibit to the coffee shop and tea room, with provision specifically included for disabled visitors, children and the elderly, as individuals or within a family unit. The concept of energy in its broadest sense is introduced at the start, using a visual and audio impact auditorium. Progressing through a multi-format explanation of natural radioactivity and the discovery of its properties, the visitor is guided along a passive learning display of non energy-related uses of radioactivity (in clinics and agriculture, etc). This provides a counterbalance to the rate of initial information availability and leaves the visitor receptive to an illuminated display of nuclear fission: this is specially designed for the younger mind but, through its effective use of mirrors, is also of interest to adults.

The production of electricity from nuclear energy is then introduced. A detailed, television-based display (using a technique known as Pepper's Ghost) is available for those seeking a greater depth of knowledge. For the younger visitor, a model reactor allows a hands-on approach to controlling power output and an introduction to the basic constraints of preliminary safety circuits. A physical break is then allowed. Sitting in a multi-video viewing room, the topical issues of economics, transport and safety are introduced. By using a long loop story, the visitor can rest at leisure with continuing input from a medium of great familiarity, geared to relaxation.

A tunnel, featuring audible safety signals used on the site, then guides the visitor to the first knowledge quiz and on into the heart of a simulated reactor. Here the mediums of sound and feel are used to great effect, exploring further the basis of reactor control. A theme park feature then follows, devoted to the issue of waste management. Finally, the visitor is guided to the largest hall, geared to providing specific and detailed information on BNFL operations. Computerised quizzes, models and passive features are liberally

scattered throughout the sound and sight displays. At the exit a range of literature is available and the visitor is invited to relax once more in a tea room, or to visit the souvenir and local produce shop.

Impressive as the whole exhibition is, further improvements are planned. Additional basic display signs (including raised lettering) are to be employed and it is hoped that an induction coil hearing aid system can be backfitted. Notwithstanding this, customer satisfaction with the facilities is already very high (more than 90 per cent are satisfied or very satisfied).[3]

Public participation

Information exchange must, by definition, be a reciprocal process. If visitors' centres are to fulfil their potential for informing and influencing the public, they must be responsive to the prevalent requirements and fashions. Opportunities for direct participation are thus an essential feature.

Questionnaires are the most obvious medium for gaining feedback. They may be incorporated in information guides, or within educational quizzes (both of which are used at the Sellafield Visitors' Centre); they may be independent leaflets; or they may be addressed direct by trained personnel. In all cases the response rate is likely to be relatively low and restricted to the most highly motivated visitors (not always the most representative).

Public participation can also be offered in other ways and the results judged both from direct feedback and from simple popularity. At Sellafield, guided coach tours of the works complex are offered in addition to the Visitors' Centre. Such tours last approximately 45 minutes and do not involve leaving the coach. Currently the take-up is around 70 per cent of all visitors and coaches generally run through the summer at around 90 per cent of seating capacity. Questions are actively encouraged and can be used to gauge the public reception. More than 95 per cent of visitors express themselves as satisfied or very satisfied with the coach and guide.[4]

Finally, the Visitors' Centre at Sellafield has experimented with a return to the Victorian tradition of public lectures explaining aspects of science and technology. This approach has run only from mid-1991 but the response so far has been encouraging. The majority of visitors have elected to attend at least one lecture during their tour (actual percentage figures are not yet available) and find it to be beneficial. In particular, the participation rate, gauged from questions arising, is higher than from any other feature of the Visitors' Centre. Perhaps this is a pointer that the most sophisticated technology cannot yet compete with a simple, personal, delivery.

The real thing

As an adjunct to the Visitors' Centre, BNFL at Sellafield maintains a policy of bringing supervised parties into the working plant. Such visits require a large organisational effort and necessarily last from four to eight hours. They are thus strenuous and require booking in advance. Notwithstanding this, some 10 per cent of all visitors request a full site tour. They represent the ultimate test of an open-door policy, by inviting people from all walks of life to become an 'inspector' for the day.

Such tours have little to offer by way of entertainment *per se* and are likely to contribute very little to the marketing success of an industry (except perhaps in the brewing and woollen trades). They are thus confined almost exclusively to the technical industries. Information can be conveyed at an intensive pace, generally in small parties and, sometimes, on a one-to-one basis.

In view of the large costs entailed, the justification for continuing site visits as an adjunct to the Visitors' Centre requires some explanation. As a technique, it allows time for persuasive argument. Where elected officials and decision-makers are concerned the costs may be written off against the need for short-term, high impact support. For notable existing or potential customers the net financial gain may be substantial. But for members of the public the justification lies mainly within a simple paradox. The offer alone is sufficient to reinforce confidence, for the vast majority, in information supplied within the Visitors' Centre, thereby obviating the necessity to attend the actual tour. It is thus a matter of experience at Sellafield that the offer of 'the real thing' remains a vital link in improving public support.

Are visitors' centres enough?

The role of the visitors' centre, together with site visits and national advertising is to gain public confidence in the industry. It remains a passive vehicle however and can be supported further by reaching out actively to seek audiences. Mobile displays at shows can reach large audiences. Establishing strong local education links creates long-term adherence. Supplying guest speakers for societies and functions gives a direct opportunity to respond to questions and address specific issues.

Each of these activities encourages an open interest in the industry and can be used as a means of inviting attendance at the visitors' centre. Once the mistrust has been cleared away, the provision of detailed information can only enlighten and inspire the enquiring mind.

Signs of success

The effectiveness of a visitors' centre or of a workplace visit is not limited to those individuals who do visit, but also to the many who are sufficiently reassured that they no longer feel the need to visit. Success must thus be measured both as a factor of the number of visitors who choose to enquire, as well as in the overall effect on public opinion.

Since 1985, the Visitors' Centre at BNFL, Sellafield, has attracted more than 600,000 visitors. In 1987 it won acclaim as the fastest growing tourist attraction in England and has gained several awards for excellence.[5] Equally importantly, opinion surveys indicate that over 90 per cent of visitors feel positively reassured as a result of their visit. Nationally, there are now indications that public acceptance of the nuclear industry is growing slowly, at a time when the popularity of coal has fallen from 54 per cent strongly in favour in 1986, to 28 per cent in 1989. Over the same period, the popularity of oil fell from 34 per cent to 22 per cent strongly in favour. By contrast, some two-thirds of the population currently believe that nuclear power will increase as part of the UK energy mix in the future, with more than one-third of the population in favour of such a policy.[6]

Whilst one visitors' centre alone cannot take the credit for this swing, the national advertising of its existence and the commitment to explaining the processes involved in the nuclear industry have certainly been of prime importance in raising public awareness. It remains to be seen whether the visitors' centre is a robust tool in maintaining levels of understanding.

Acknowledgements

I am indebted to all those within the Public Relations Department at Sellafield who staff the

Visitors' Centre and organise or undertake the supporting activities. Particular thanks are due to the many retired staff, from all parts of the company, who have returned willingly to pass their experiences and knowledge on to all enquiring visitors.

Figure 1. The role of the visitors' centre in industry

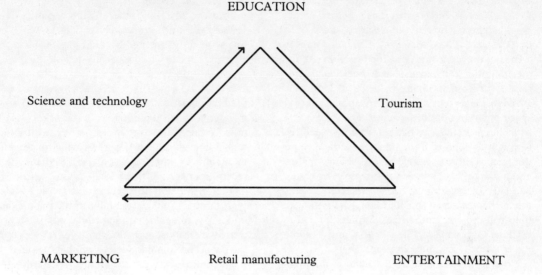

Notes and references

1 Wilson, E O, *Sociobiology: A New Synthesis* (Cambridge, MA: Harvard University Press, 1975)
2 Personal communication given by the Royal Society for the Prevention of Accidents in 1991
3 MORI, *Attitudes towards Sellafield Visitors' Centre* (research conducted for BNFL, 1990)
4 *ibid*
5 Yearbook statistics for 1986 to 1987 from the English Tourist Board
6 MORI and GALLUP opinion polls, 1989

Jodrell Bank Visitor Centre

Sylvia Chaplin and Francis Graham-Smith

Readers of the *Guardian* were startled in 1967 by the headline, 'A challenge to stately homes'. This heralded the opening of our Visitor Centre, called in those days 'The Concourse'. The name indicated a kind of universal but undefined usefulness, a meeting place for scientists and the public. The idea dated from 1964, at the height of Jodrell Bank's fame as part of the American and Soviet space programmes. In the summer of that year Manchester University had set up a marquee for a fortnight to cope with the popular demand to see the famous radio telescope and to hear something about its purposes and achievements. The response had been overwhelming: 35,000 visitors, crowding the narrow entrance lane and filling buckets with their half-crown entrance fees. Something had to be done to provide for the demand, and to allow the research to continue in peace.

Now, 25 years on, and 2.5 million visitors later, we are still asking ourselves what we should be doing, and how we should be doing it. Our main purposes are to educate and to inform. We know now that we must also set out to entertain: we must attract a wider public than those who are already scientists or sympathetic to science. Above all we realise that we have a unique opportunity for introducing children to modern science; an opportunity and a responsibility to make science exciting, interesting, and accessible. About 150,000 visitors now come, including about 35,000 school-children. These must be our real target, although we also acknowledge a responsibility to inform the taxpayer how his or her money is spent; after all, it is the taxpayer who ultimately pays for astronomy in this country.

We have to be realistic: it is no use setting out to change the whole perception of science in every visitor who spends a couple of hours at Jodrell Bank. Of course we should be showing that science pervades the whole of life, that it provides essential skills both in intellectual thought and in practical activity, that it provides career opportunities and academic challenge. But we like to think that sometimes some wider glimmer of light will dawn. How can we make this happen?

In the first few years the visitor was confronted with informative but rather highbrow panels describing the current research work at Jodrell. This was soon supplemented by examples of discarded electronics boxes, no longer needed on the telescope. All this has been swept away. There is of course an information panel on the discovery of the first planet outside the solar system, and an interactive video presentation of the MERLIN telescope network. We start, however, with the school curriculum, and try to provide for teaching to attainment target 16 (as it was). Perhaps the most important aid is the Planetarium, which is second in size and attendance only to the London Planetarium. The latest exhibit in the main exhibition is a spectacular rotating Earth, sunlit, showing time, the seasons, and sunlight at Jodrell through the day. The Sundial Society will help us take this theme outside into the Arboretum, where there already is a large-scale model of the solar system to explore.

The link between radio and optical astronomy is made in many ways: there is a speaking model of Isaac Newton expounding the effect of a prism and speculating about X-rays and radio; there are photographs of astronomical objects alongside maps of their radio emission; there is a steerable radio telescope picking up radio waves from the Sun. There is also a link to be made between radio science and modern practical life: we use the theme of satellites and their use in communications.

The importance of involvement, which may or may not mean interaction, cannot be overemphasised. A child who actually steers a radio telescope, or who rolls a ball down a gravity well, may not know exactly what he or she is doing: one day, however, the light may dawn ('That's what I did at Jodrell'). Push-buttons, however, are an invention of the devil. Our new rotating Earth, for example, is designed to portray the inclination of the Earth's axis, and the season is made to change by rotating the whole model. This was, of course, set up with a push-button; on the opening day the whole model was in continuous rotation as every enthusiast fought to get a finger on the button. The button now has a built-in time lapse which can only be overridden by demonstrators. A serious loss? No, the exhibit is fascinating: it works and the visitor is usually completely involved by watching.

Interactive exhibits must be indestructible: we have no time or money to keep repairing broken equipment. (The Centre is entirely self-financed, relying only on gate money from our 150,000 visitors). The ideal is represented by the 'whispering gallery', the two paraboloids facing one another about 50m apart: the only problem here is excessive wear on the grass between the two dishes. Even better are holograms: here interaction consists of trying to grasp the image in the air, and the image is totally non-destructible.

Staffing is, unfortunately, only minimal, with only four full-time posts. The top priority is schools visits; here our Schools Liaison Officer can usually escort and help curriculum work. There is a small army of part-timers. These should be trained and recruited to help in the same way with schools visits, as has been achieved in other centres. Unfortunately, so far, we have not been able to do this.

The Visitor Centre operates independently of the main Jodrell research laboratories. This is essential for both sides: on the one hand we have some of the busiest people in the world trying to push out the frontiers of knowledge while carrying a full university teaching load, while on the other we have a professional and specialised activity which is very different from research and very different from university teaching. In practice, of course, there is close liaison and co-operation. The Visitor Centre is only there because of the radio observatory, and the research side is devoted to the advancement of science through teaching as much as through research. The joint authorship of this paper is some indication of the practical importance of our partnership.